SPOTLIGHT ON LITERACY

READ ALOUDS
PLAYS AND CHORAL READINGS

Grade 4

Margaret H. Lippert
Anthologist

As part of Macmillan/McGraw-Hill's effort to help make a difference in the environment, this anthology has been printed on recycled paper.

10% post-consumer content

Macmillan McGraw-Hill

New York • Farmington

Macmillan/McGraw-Hill

A Division of The **McGraw·Hill** *Companies*

Macmillan/McGraw-Hill
1221 Avenue of the Americas
New York, New York 10020

Printed in the United States of America

ISBN 0-02-181286-1 / 4

2 3 4 5 6 7 8 9   P O H   02 01 00 99 98 97

This book is dedicated to you, the teacher, who will pick the words of these stories up off the page and send them into the hearts and minds of your students, and to you, the listeners, who will take the words and build them into images.

MARGARET H. LIPPERT

CONTENTS

4

PLAYS, CHORAL READINGS

READERS THEATER PLAYS

WRITE YOUR OWN

CHORAL READINGS

INTRODUCTION

by Margaret H. Lippert

Long before I wrote stories, I listened for stories. Listening for them is something more acute than listening to them. I suppose it's an early form of participation in what goes on. Listening children know stories are there. When their elders sit and begin, children are just waiting and hoping for one to come out, like a mouse from its hole.

EUDORA WELTY[1]

This book is stuffed with mice. Your students are waiting.

You are part of a long tradition of storytellers and story readers. Stories belong to us all. From ancient times, people have been entertained and nourished by stories. All of us in our own families and culture have, like Eudora Welty, been entranced by the tales that have been told to us from the time we first started to listen. From these stories, we learned about listening and speaking and then about reading—connecting the images and messages of stories with print and with books.

The power of stories draws us to ideas and thoughts and feelings that we want and need to explore. Through stories we learn about the experiences of others and come to understand ourselves better. The best stories take us from where we are and lead us, word by word, image by image, into places known and unknown, familiar and new, comfortable and exciting.

Reading aloud opens students to a new way of learning— listening. Many of us, and many of our students, are unaccustomed to listening carefully. We tune out much of what goes on around us. We need to remember the power of listening and help our students do the same.

Reading aloud can grip students in a listening vise—because they want to know what will happen next, they listen with fully focused attention. Since students can understand a much larger vocabulary than they can read themselves, when we read aloud we expose them to more sophisticated concepts and content than they could read independently. People of traditional cultures knew this—they passed on knowledge through their stories.

As you read aloud, you give your students stories and something of yourself. You build a community in your classroom that links you and your students to one another, to the story, and to the thinking and feeling of the author and the culture from which that story springs. Your students stretch and grow, discovering the pathways and journeys of others and, in the process, making discoveries of their own.

A READ-ALOUD CELEBRATION

Each Read Aloud in this collection relates in some way—theme, style, author, content—to a selection in the Macmillan/McGraw-Hill Reading/Language Arts student anthologies. Many of the Read Alouds are traditional tales, stories that were handed down from one generation to another within a particular culture. Traditional stories include folk tales, fairy tales, myths, legends, tall tales, and fables. In addition to traditional literature, classics and contemporary literature are represented.

In order to root this collection in the traditional oral heritage from which stories spring, I interviewed people who grew up in storytelling cultures and taped them telling stories so that you and your students would have access to their wisdom and to their stories. Some of these gifted storytellers are included on the SONGS AND STORIES AUDIOCASSETTES that are offered with the series.

The information about the contributors and the indexes at the end of the collection provide important information for you to share with your students about the origins of the tales and of the tellers.

It is preferable, though not absolutely necessary, to skim through a story before you read it aloud. That way you will know where the story is headed, and you can adjust your reading style to the mood and rhythm of the story.

As you read, take your time and read with involvement and intensity. Your students will need time to construct story images and to process ideas as the story moves along. To help you judge the time you will need to allow for each story reading, the range of times it took several different teachers to read each story aloud to a group of students is included in the CONTENTS.

Sometimes questions will arise in response to a story. When this happens, I often ask students if they can answer the questions that have been raised. I have done this countless times, and, no matter how difficult the question, no student has ever said, "I don't know." Within the story's context, they do know, and they help one another explore the answers to their own questions.

Now I often ask after reading or telling a story, "Was there any part of the story that was unclear to you?" or "What did you wonder about as you listened to the story?" There are always many questions. And frequently there are many answers to a question. The harder the question, the more ideas and responses the question seems to generate. For example, after hearing me tell *Yeh-Shen*,[2] which is a Chinese version of the Cinderella story, one third grader asked, "Why did the stepmother kill the fish?" Seven children offered seven different explanations. Some of the responses were as follows: "Maybe she didn't like the fish." "One of the reasons could be that she wanted the meat from the fish. Or that she didn't want the girl [Yeh-Shen] to be friends with the fish." "I think she was just plain mean."

The students listened to the story. They struggled with parts that were unclear or unexplained, and they integrated all of their previous knowledge with the information generated in the story. They also developed plausible explanations to justify the actions of the characters and the events in the story.

In an atmosphere where questions are encouraged, hard questions are more likely to rise to the surface so they can be explored. Every question is a new starting point. Through ALL their questions, students seek meaning and struggle collaboratively to find answers to their own puzzling questions about the stories. What a wonderful model for seeking responses to the puzzling questions that confront them in their lives.

"I DO AND I UNDERSTAND"

There is an ancient Chinese proverb: "I hear and I forget. I see and I remember. I do and I understand."

By reading these stories aloud, you make them part of the oral tradition. Just listening to these stories will enrich the imaginations of your students, offering them new ideas and insights. But if your students re-create a favorite story in another form, it will become theirs in an even deeper way. "Doing" the stories leads to further understanding and appreciation of them.

Your students may wish to retell the story as a group in their own words, or to illustrate or depict the story in paintings, collages, or dioramas. They may enjoy spontaneously reenacting the story without props or scenery, or perhaps with the simplest of these. They may choose to write their favorite or least favorite part of the story, or their own version of the story either in whole or in part. If they do any of these things, either prompted by you or motivated on their own, they will know the story more intimately. The better they know the story, the more comfortable they will feel with it, and the better they will like it. The more they like it, the more they will want to share it, perhaps even outside the classroom, with family or friends. Thus the oral tradition continues.

ONWARD TO STORYTELLING

As a storyteller and story lover, I would be remiss if I did not encourage you to try telling, without the text, a tale or two. Telling a story is fun. It also models for students the possibility that they, too, can recall, retell, and enjoy stories whenever they wish. If you've told stories before, you know the flexibility and closeness engendered by direct contact with listeners, without an intervening page. If you haven't, you could begin with a short, familiar tale.

13

You don't need to memorize the words to enjoy telling stories. In fact, memorizing the words may distract you from the images and sequence of the tale itself. I simply picture the story as it takes place, then describe it to my listeners as I "see" it. This is the same skill you use when relating an anecdote that happened to you or when telling a joke. As a teacher, you already know how to hold the attention of your class. Storytelling is one small step beyond explaining a concept or describing an assignment.

The author-storyteller-artist Ashley Bryan has a favorite African proverb: "He who learns, teaches!" Learn the craft of storytelling along with your students. Allow them to watch you struggle and try and learn. Make mistakes and work through your mistakes. Allow them also to watch you as you succeed and soar on the wings of new stories. This will teach them about your love of story and language, and about how much you are willing to risk for them.

ENDINGS AND BEGINNINGS

From here, it is up to you. The stories are yours now. Read them, enjoy them, pass them along. By sharing these stories with your students, you will preserve them for at least one more generation.

Since this is a book of stories, I'd like to end this introduction with a story, or to be more accurate, a part of a Russian folk tale that is my favorite story. The oldest man in the village, encouraging a young boy to tell his first story to the expectant listeners around the fire, says:

A story is a letter that comes to us from yesterday. Each person who tells it adds his word to the message and sends it on to tomorrow. So begin.

from "The Tale of the Tales"[3]

[1] Eudora Welty, *One Writer's Beginnings* (Cambridge, MA: Harvard University Press, 1983), p. 16.

[2] Ai-Ling Louie, *Yeh-Shen: A Cinderella Story from China* (New York: Philomel Books, 1982).

[3] George and Helen Papashvily, "The Tale of the Tales," *Yes and No Stories: A Book of Georgian Folk Tales* (New York: Harper & Brothers, 1946).

I can promise that once you begin the daily experience of reading aloud to children, it will become one of the best parts of your day and the children's day, minutes and hours that will be treasured for years to come.

JIM TRELEASE
from *The Read-Aloud Handbook*

15

The Dancing Granny

*a folk tale from the West Indies
retold by Ashley Bryan*

There was an old woman who lived in a hut. Everyone called her Granny Anika.

She sang her songs and she stirred her pot. She licked the ladle and tasted her stew. Umm-yum! She beat the sides of the calabash, pom-pa-lom! pom-pa-lom!

Granny Anika was a happy old lady. She woke up singing. All day long she sang and beat out rhythms on anything within reach. She rapped with sticks, she drummed with spoons, she tapped with ladles and she hummed dance tunes to the beat of her knives.

> *"Shake it to the East,
> Shake it to the West."*

But what Granny Anika loved best of all was to dance. She danced in the morning. She danced at noon. She danced till the sun set. And then at night she dreamed dance dreams and danced in her sleep till dawn.

That old lady was never too busy or too tired to do a little dance. She cleared a vegetable patch near her hut and sang as she hoed the ground. She kept step to the chop, chop, chop of her hoe.

The seeds stirred in the earth to the vibrations of Granny's song and dance. The vegetables came up strong to the gentle slap, pitter-pat of Old Anika's bare feet.

Granny Anika was proud of her grounds. She set in a good variety of seeds and raised all of her provisions. She sang:

"Mama loves peas,
Papa loves corn,
Baby loves beans
Sure as you're born.
Put in potatoes,
Granny loves yam,
Don't forget okra,
Beets and jam."

Jam! Well, Granny picked sweet berries from bushes and made a thick brew, which she spread on sliced yam and called jam.

Granny Anika did her share of work, and she did her dance. Uh-huh! She snapped her fingers and clapped her hands. Uh-huh! She knew her song, and she got along.

Uh-huh!

One day Spider Ananse came strutting on by Granny Anika's hut.

You couldn't imagine a lazier fellow than Brother Ananse. He'd strut and stroll all day long, looking like he was doing something important. But Spider wouldn't work.

No kind of tune could make the hoe feel lighter in Brother Ananse's hands. And no kind of beat eased his long, slim feet on a spade dug into the ground.

Spider Ananse preferred resting and loafing and lounging and wandering around until he found someone he might trick for his dinner.

Spider watched Granny Anika working in her field. She was bent over the hoe doing a jig as she dug. She didn't see Spider Ananse climb into a tree.

Spider Ananse peeped out at Granny from behind the tree trunk. "Hmm . . ." he thought, "I won't get a thing from that great garden patch if Granny doesn't go."

17

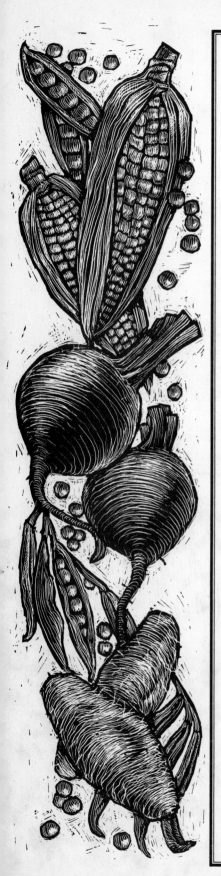

Brother Ananse began to sing. He sang one of his catchiest tunes. He broke off a twig and rapped out a marked dance beat on a dead branch.

> *"Pom-pa-lom!*
> *Pom-pa-lom!*
> *Papa's here*
> *And Mama's gone.*
> *I sing, you dance, my dee-dee.*
> *You dance, I sing, my swee-tee.*
> *I'll trouble you, my dee-dee,*
> *I'll trouble you, my la-dy."*

Granny heard the tune and hummed it to herself. "Umm-hmm! Sweet, sweet, sweet," she sang.

Then the music and the beat got to Granny's feet. She held her hoe like a partner and swung with it to the right. She swung to the left.

Spider Ananse sang out:

> *"Shake it to the East,*
> *Shake it to the West,*
> *Shake it to the very one*
> *That you love the best."*

Granny Anika skipped like a little girl. She flung out her arms, dropping the hoe, and danced off the field.

Spider Ananse sang louder and louder and rapped harder and harder.

Granny Anika wheeled to the East. She wheeled to the West. She let the music take her, and the dance carried her off. Away she wheeled northwards, head over heels, until she disappeared from sight.

Then Brother Ananse dropped down from the tree laughing till he shook.

"There goes the dancing Granny." He laughed. "Man! She sure looked like a tumbleweed as she wheeled by."

Spider helped himself to all the corn he could carry and carted it off to his house.

His wife said, "Good corn."

His mother said, "Sure as you're born."

That night they all sat down to heaping platefuls of steaming corn.

When Granny Anika finally came out of her dance right side up, she was eleven miles north of her village.

"O my! O my!" she cried. "I know that voice. It was Brother Ananse. He sure can sing. Now why didn't he come dance with me? Anyway, I got a good dance to the North."

Back home, Granny went to her field and saw that her corn crop was ravished.

"Eh, eh! That good-for-nothing, no 'count Spider Ananse! He sure tricked me. So, that's why he didn't try to match my steps! But I'll catch him. Next time he comes I won't let the music sweet me so."

Sure enough, Spider Ananse soon came round again to plunder Granny's vegetable patch.

"Umm-yum," he thought as he looked out over the pretty field. "If the corn tasted so good, I wonder how Granny's peas and beans might be."

Spider Ananse climbed into the tree and began to sing:

> *"Ah mini lah lee lee*
> *Again I'm in the country*
> *'Cause Nana's corn*
> *Tastes good to me.*
> *I see those beans,*
> *I see those greens,*
> *I see those beets,*
> *Fit for kings and queens."*

"See what you see and see what you like and have a fit too," said Granny, " 'cause that see and that fit is all you're going to get. You can sing for beans and sing for peas for all I care. It's going to take two to dance to your tune today." Granny shuffled her feet lightly. "Yeah! Take a good look. You'll see that your Mama lives right here, and she don't plan to go nowhere. Uh-uh, no wheres away. Not this here day."

Spider laughed and did some variations on his rapping. Then he went into his big song:

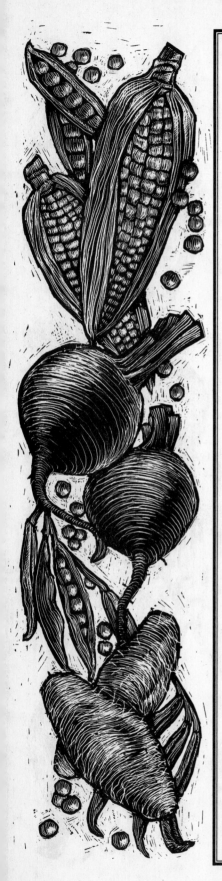

"Pom-pa-lom!
Pom-pa-lom!
Papa's here
But Mama's gone.
I sing for peas,
I sing for corn.
You plant, I'll pull,
Sure as you're born."

Granny Anika held her hoe tightly and dug her toes into the ground.

Spider sang on:

"I sing, you dance, my dee-dee.
You dance, I sing, my swee-tee.
I trouble you, my dee-dee,
I trouble you, my la-dy."

Granny kicked up her feet and dropped the hoe.
Spider sang:

"O! Shake it to the East
Shake it to the West,
Shake it to the very one
That you love the best."

Granny's feet could no longer resist Spider's beat. She wheeled to the East, she wheeled to the West. Then head over heels, she cartwheeled southwards.

"Man, if Granny don't spin like a thistle on the breath of a whistle," laughed Spider, dropping out of the tree. He watched the dancing Granny twirl out of sight.

Then Spider filled his bag with peas and beans and strutted all the way home.

Spider's wife said, "Good beans, good peas."

Spider's mother said, "If you please."

That night they all sat down to heaping gourds of hot beans and peas.

Granny Anika found herself twelve miles south of her village before she danced Spider's tune out of her feet.

When she got back home, she saw that Spider Ananse had stolen her peas and beans.

"How can I catch that thieving rascal?" she said. "Brother Ananse sings the danciest tunes. I just can't stay still when the music sweets me so. That I know. Trouble is, Spider knows it too."

Spider Ananse came again and climbed into the tree. He stayed well out of reach of Granny, but his voice reached Granny Anika well.

"Put your hands on your hips
And let your backbone shake."

Once Spider got into his song, Granny couldn't resist. She danced to the North. She danced to the South. And when Spider sang the pom-pa-lom part, Granny was into her steps.

"Shake it to the East,
Shake it to the West."

Granny was now dancing her best and pleased as could be with her style. Even Spider Ananse had to admire her as she went, head over heels, cartwheeling westwards.

"That dancing Granny turns like a windmill!" he exclaimed. "She sure can twirl her arms and legs in time to the tune."

Spider took all the potatoes he could carry and toted the sack home.

Spider's wife said, "Good potatoes."

Spider's mother said, "Tastier than tomatoes."

That night they all sat down to a heaping mound of roasted potatoes.

Granny had a good dance, it's true. She came to a stop thirteen miles to the west of her village and returned home.

The fourth time Spider Ananse came by, he started singing before he was well into the tree.

"Pom-pa-lom!
Pom-pa-lom!
Papa's hungry
And Mama's not home."

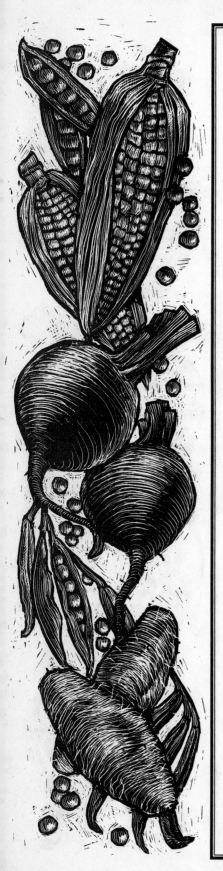

Granny started her dance. She swayed to the South. She swayed to the North.

> *"Shake it to the East,*
> *Shake it to the West."*

"Sweet, sweet, sweet," sang Granny to the beat.

Spider didn't even have to finish his song. Granny heard well, and the tune was wheeling in her. Off she went, heels over head, wheeling eastwards.

Spider Ananse shook his head and said, "No one can outdance dancing Granny. She spins like a top."

He filled his basket with beets and beat it on back home.

Spider's wife said, "Good beets."

Spider's mother said, "Sweeter than sweets."

That night they all sat down to big bowls of boiled beets.

Granny Anika danced to a stop, right side up fourteen miles to the east of her village.

"My," she said, "that was the sweetest dance of all."

When she got home, Granny sat by her hut. She tapped her foot as she looked out over her ravished field.

"Look at that, will you?" she said. "Trickster Spider's done taken my corn, my peas and beans, my potatoes and my beets. I'll never catch that clever character as long as he swings on that sweet song."

So Granny Anika gathered in all that was left of her vegetables. There was nothing more in the fields for Brother Ananse to steal.

When Spider Ananse sauntered by again, he was so sure of himself that he started singing his song long before he reached the tree. Now what did he do that for?

Granny Anika was waiting for just such a chance. Quickly she swung her hoe and caught Brother Ananse around the waist. She pulled him to her and held onto him as if he were the first dance partner she ever had.

"Let go! Let go of me," Spider cried.

"I've got you now, you singing brother," said Granny. "Dance with me. To the East, to the West, to the North, to the South. Sing your song."

Granny Anika pinched Spider, and he began to sing:

"Pom-pa-lom!
Pom-pa-lom!
I ate your peas,
I ate your corn."

"Sure as you're born, you did. Now dance, Brother! Dance!" sang Granny to the song. "I'll teach you that two can trip to that tune too."

Granny Anika led Spider Ananse in the dance. They whirled and they twirled to the wheeling beat. Every time that Spider tried to stop, Granny squeezed him tighter.

They danced to the North.

They danced to the South.

Now Spider's feet felt the sweet beat of Granny's steps. Together they sang:

"Shake it to the East,
Shake it to the West,
Shake it to the very one
That you love the best."

They wheeled to the East.

They whirled to the West.

They heeled to the North.

They twirled to the South.

Off they went capering and cartwheeling away!

Pom-pa-lom!

Pom-pa-lom!

Spider Ananse didn't get one vegetable from Granny Anika that day, but he sure got one good dance with the old woman.

Dancing Granny never had a better partner than Spider Ananse. They danced more miles together than Granny had ever danced alone. And if Spider's still singing, then they're still dancing.

"Dance Granny! You move like the river."
"Dance Spider! Let's dance forever."
"Dance, Granny! As the lead bends
"The dance goes on, but the story ends."

/Kaggan Brings the Fire

a Bushman story from South Africa, collected by P.J. Schoeman, retold by Melissa Heckler

[*The / before /Kaggan's name represents a click in the Bushman language.*]

Long, long ago, back in the time when animals were people, Ostrich lived by himself. He had fire. At that time other people did not know about fire. They slept in the darkness and ate their food raw.

Ostrich's camp was the only place where there was fire. He made fire and when he had enough glowing coals and ashes, he took the fire and hid it under his wings. He did not want to share his secret with other people.

Grandfather /Kaggan, the great magician, who in those days lived alone with his wife and two children, went out one day to hunt for food. He came across Ostrich's camp and found Ostrich busy roasting bulbs and meat over a small fire. Ostrich gave /Kaggan some of the cooked food. /Kaggan ate, and as soon as he tasted the delicious food, great plans started forming in his mind. He said good-bye to Ostrich. He pretended to leave, but instead he hid behind a bush, and watched how Ostrich hid the coals under his wings. Then /Kaggan went home.

When /Kaggan met his wife, Dassie, he said to her, "We always eat raw food, but

24

Ostrich today gave me food cooked over a fire. It tasted so nice that I didn't even want to talk while I ate!"

After that, Dassie gave him no peace. So they moved to Ostrich's camp. /Kaggan announced to Ostrich, "We have come to dance!"

That night, they danced. But Ostrich was clever and danced with his wings close to his body. But /Kaggan was a clever magician. He shouted to Ostrich, "Do not hide your beautiful wings like that. My wife wants to see them. Dance with wide-spread wings."

That was not all he said.

"A handsome man like you must dance in front. I, who am not so handsome, will dance in back of you."

Ostrich then danced with the tips of his wings open. /Kaggan groaned, "If you dance like that, my wife will think I have lied. Here, you with your long beautiful neck, you dance in front of me. I with my short ugly neck will dance in back of you. Show my wife your wings."

So Ostrich danced with his wings opened just a *little* bit wider. /Kaggan called out, "If you dance like that you will be the death of me. Open your wings wide and show my wife how beautiful they are!"

Ostrich then lifted his wings wide open. /Kaggan ran forward and grabbed the coals of fire and fled to the open veld. Ostrich sped after him. When /Kaggan saw that Ostrich was close on his heels, he stopped and scattered the coals of fire across the face of the earth shouting, "All my people must have fire."

Since that day, fires have spread across the face of the earth. All people have fire. And sometimes after that, Grandfather /Kaggan was known as Old Tinderbox, the firebringer.

THE SEARCH FOR THE MAGIC LAKE

a folk tale from Ecuador
retold by Genevieve Barlow

Long ago there was a ruler of the vast Inca Empire who had an only son. This youth brought great joy to his father's heart but also a sadness, for the prince had been born in ill health.

As the years passed the prince's health did not improve, and none of the court doctors could find a cure for his illness.

One night the aged emperor went down on his knees and prayed at the altar.

"O Great Ones," he said, "I am getting older and will soon leave my people and join you in the heavens. There is no one to look after them but my son, the prince. I pray you make him well and strong so he can be a fit ruler for my people. Tell me how his malady can be cured."

The emperor put his head in his hands and waited for an answer. Soon he heard a voice coming from the fire that burned constantly in front of the altar.

"Let the prince drink water from the magic lake at the end of the world," the voice said, "and he will be well."

At that moment the fire sputtered and died. Among the cold ashes lay a golden flask.

But the emperor was much too old to make the long journey to the end of the world, and the young prince was too ill to travel. So the emperor proclaimed that whosoever should fill the golden flask with the magic water would be greatly rewarded.

Many brave men set out to search for the magic lake, but none could find it. Days and weeks passed and still the flask remained empty.

In a valley, some distance from the emperor's palace, lived a poor farmer who had a wife, two grown sons, and a young daughter.

One day the older son said to his father, "Let my brother and me join in the search for the magic lake. Before the moon is new again, we shall return and help you harvest the corn and potatoes."

The father remained silent. He was not thinking of the harvest, but feared for his sons' safety.

When the father did not answer, the second son added, "Think of the rich reward, Father!"

"It is their duty to go," said his wife, "for we must all try to help our emperor and the young prince."

After his wife had spoken, the father yielded.

"Go if you must, but beware of the wild beasts and evil spirits," he cautioned.

With their parents' blessing, and an affectionate farewell from their young sister, the sons set out on their journey.

They found many lakes, but none where the sky touched the water.

Finally the younger brother said, "Before another day has passed we must return to help father with the harvest."

"Yes," agreed the other, "but I have thought of a plan. Let us each carry a jar of water from any lake along the way. We can say it will cure the prince. Even if it doesn't, surely the emperor will give us a small reward for our trouble."

"Agreed," said the younger brother.

On arriving at the palace, the deceitful youths told the emperor and his court that they brought water from the magic lake. At once the prince was given a sip from each of the brothers' jars, but of course he remained as ill as before.

"Perhaps the water must be sipped from the golden flask," one of the high priests said.

But the golden flask would not hold the water. In some mysterious way the water from the jars disappeared as soon as it was poured into the flask.

In despair the emperor called for his magician and said to him, "Can you break the spell of the flask so the water will remain for my son to drink?"

"I cannot do that, your majesty," replied the magician. "But I believe," he added wisely, "that the flask is telling us that we have been deceived by the two brothers. The flask can be filled only with water from the magic lake."

When the brothers heard this, they trembled with fright, for they knew their falsehood was discovered.

So angry was the emperor that he ordered the brothers thrown into chains. Each day they were forced to drink water from their jars as a reminder of their false deed. News of their disgrace spread far and wide.

Again the emperor sent messengers throughout the land pleading for someone to bring the magic water before death claimed him and the young prince.

Súmac, the little sister of the deceitful youths, was tending her flock of llamas when she heard the sound of the royal trumpet. Then came the voice of the emperor's servant with his urgent message from the court.

Quickly the child led her llamas home and begged her parents to let her go in search of the magic water.

"You are too young," her father said. "Besides, look at what has already befallen your brothers. Some evil spirit must have taken hold of them to make them tell such a lie."

And her mother said, "We could not bear to be without our precious Súmac!"

"But think how sad our emperor will be if the young prince dies," replied the innocent child. "And if I can find the magic lake, perhaps the emperor will forgive my brothers and send them home."

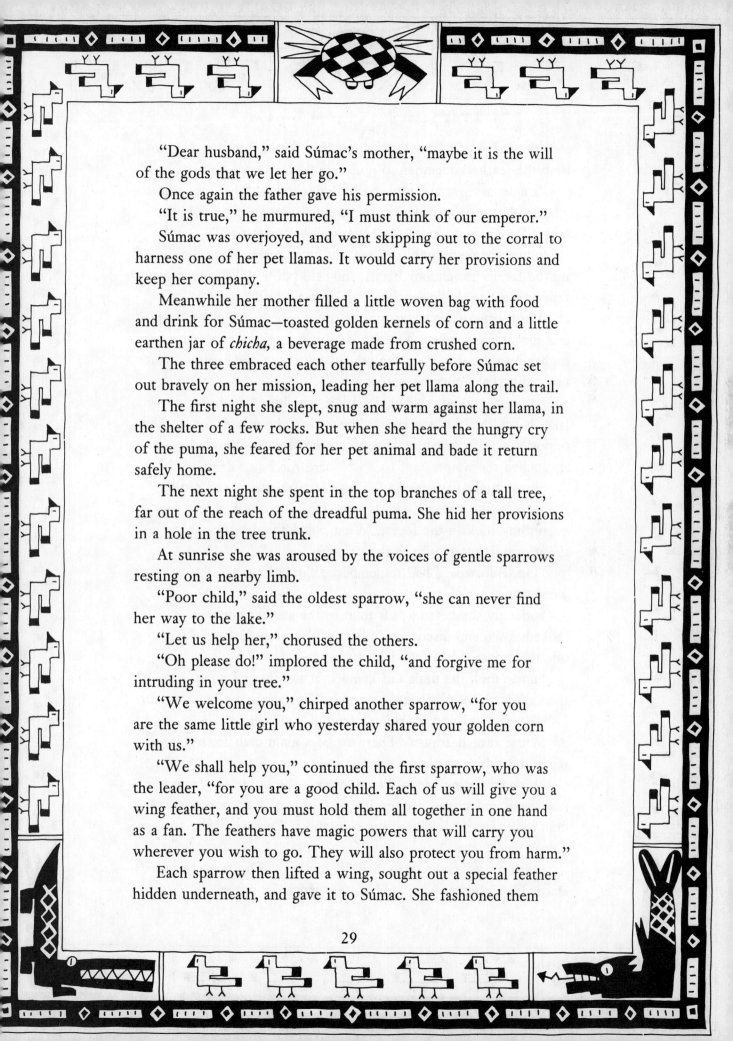

"Dear husband," said Súmac's mother, "maybe it is the will of the gods that we let her go."

Once again the father gave his permission.

"It is true," he murmured, "I must think of our emperor."

Súmac was overjoyed, and went skipping out to the corral to harness one of her pet llamas. It would carry her provisions and keep her company.

Meanwhile her mother filled a little woven bag with food and drink for Súmac—toasted golden kernels of corn and a little earthen jar of *chicha*, a beverage made from crushed corn.

The three embraced each other tearfully before Súmac set out bravely on her mission, leading her pet llama along the trail.

The first night she slept, snug and warm against her llama, in the shelter of a few rocks. But when she heard the hungry cry of the puma, she feared for her pet animal and bade it return safely home.

The next night she spent in the top branches of a tall tree, far out of the reach of the dreadful puma. She hid her provisions in a hole in the tree trunk.

At sunrise she was aroused by the voices of gentle sparrows resting on a nearby limb.

"Poor child," said the oldest sparrow, "she can never find her way to the lake."

"Let us help her," chorused the others.

"Oh please do!" implored the child, "and forgive me for intruding in your tree."

"We welcome you," chirped another sparrow, "for you are the same little girl who yesterday shared your golden corn with us."

"We shall help you," continued the first sparrow, who was the leader, "for you are a good child. Each of us will give you a wing feather, and you must hold them all together in one hand as a fan. The feathers have magic powers that will carry you wherever you wish to go. They will also protect you from harm."

Each sparrow then lifted a wing, sought out a special feather hidden underneath, and gave it to Súmac. She fashioned them into the shape of a little fan, taking the ribbon from her hair to bind the feathers together so none would be lost.

"I must warn you," said the oldest sparrow, "that the lake is guarded by three terrible creatures. But have no fear. Hold the magic fan up to your face and you will be unharmed."

Súmac thanked the birds over and over again. Then, holding up the fan in her chubby hands, she said politely, "Please, magic fan, take me to the lake at the end of the world."

A soft breeze swept her out of the top branches of the tree and through the valley. Then up she was carried, higher and higher into the sky, until she could look down and see the great mountain peaks covered with snow.

At last the wind put her down on the shore of a beautiful lake. It was, indeed, the lake at the end of the world, for, on the opposite side from where she stood, the sky came down so low it touched the water.

Súmac tucked the magic fan into her waistband and ran to the edge of the water. Suddenly her face fell. She had left everything back in the forest. What could she use for carrying the precious water back to the prince?

"Oh, I do wish I had remembered the jar!" she said, weeping.

Suddenly she heard a soft thud in the sand at her feet. She looked down and discovered a beautiful golden flask—the same one the emperor had found in the ashes.

Súmac took the flask and kneeled at the water's edge. Just then a hissing voice behind her said, "Get away from my lake or I shall wrap my long, hairy legs around your neck."

Súmac turned around. There stood a giant crab as large as a pig and as black as night.

With trembling hands the child took the magic fan from her waistband and spread it open in front of her face. As soon as the crab looked at it, he closed his eyes and fell down on the sand in a deep sleep.

Once more Súmac started to fill the flask. This time she was startled by a fierce voice bubbling up from the water.

"Get away from my lake or I shall eat you," gurgled a giant green alligator. His long tail beat the water angrily.

Súmac waited until the creature swam closer. Then she held up the fan. The alligator blinked. He drew back. Slowly, quietly, he sank to the bottom of the lake in a sound sleep.

Before Súmac could recover from her fright, she heard a shrill whistle in the air. She looked up and saw a flying serpent. His skin was red as blood. Sparks flew from his eyes.

"Get away from my lake or I shall bite you," hissed the serpent as it batted its wings around her head.

Again Súmac's fan saved her from harm. The serpent closed his eyes and drifted to the ground. He folded his wings and coiled up on the sand. Then he began to snore.

Súmac sat for a moment to quiet herself. Then, realizing that the danger was past, she sighed with great relief.

"Now I can fill the golden flask and be on my way," she said to herself.

When this was done, she held the flask tightly in one hand and clutched the fan in the other.

"Please take me to the palace," she said.

Hardly were the words spoken, when she found herself safely in front of the palace gates. She looked at the tall guard.

"I wish to see the emperor," Súmac uttered in trembling tones.

"Why, little girl?" the guard asked kindly.

"I bring water from the magic lake to cure the prince."

The guard looked down at her in astonishment.

"Come!" he commanded in a voice loud and deep as thunder.

In just a few moments Súmac was led into a room full of sadness. The emperor was pacing up and down in despair. The prince lay motionless on a huge bed. His eyes were closed and his face was without color. Beside him knelt his mother, weeping.

Without wasting words, Súmac went to the prince and gave him a few drops of magic water. Soon he opened his eyes. His cheeks became flushed. It was not long before he sat up in bed. He drank some more.

"How strong I feel!" the prince cried joyfully.

The emperor and his wife embraced Súmac. Then Súmac told them of her adventurous trip to the lake. They praised her courage. They marveled at the reappearance of the golden flask and at the powers of the magic fan.

"Dear child," said the emperor, "all the riches of my empire are not enough to repay you for saving my son's life. Ask what you will and it shall be yours."

"Oh, generous emperor," said Súmac timidly, "I have but three wishes."

"Name them and they shall be yours," urged the emperor.

"First, I wish my brothers to be free to return to my parents. They have learned their lesson and will never be false again. I know they were only thinking of a reward for my parents. Please forgive them."

"Guards, free them at once!" ordered the emperor.

"Secondly, I wish the magic fan returned to the forest so the sparrows may have their feathers again."

This time the emperor had no time to speak. Before anyone in the room could utter a sound, the magic fan lifted itself up, spread itself wide open, and floated out the window toward the woods. Everyone watched in amazement. When the fan was out of sight, they applauded.

"What is your last wish, dear Súmac?" asked the queen mother.

"I wish that my parents be given a large farm and great flocks of llamas, vicuñas, and alpacas, so they will not be poor any longer."

"It will be so," said the emperor, "but I am sure your parents never considered themselves poor with so wonderful a daughter."

"Won't you stay with us in the palace?" ventured the prince.

"Yes, stay with us!" urged the emperor and his wife. "We will do everything to make you happy."

"Oh thank you," said Súmac blushing happily, "but I must return to my parents and to my brothers. I miss them as I know they have missed me. They do not even know I am safe, for I came directly to your palace."

The royal family did not try to detain Súmac any longer.

"My own guard will see that you get home safely," said the emperor.

When she reached home, she found that all she had wished for had come to pass: her brothers were waiting for her with their parents; a beautiful house and huge barn were being constructed; her father had received a deed granting him many acres of new, rich farmland.

Súmac ran into the arm of her happy family.

At the palace, the golden flask was never empty. Each time it was used, it was refilled. Thus the prince's royal descendants never suffered ill health and the kingdom remained strong.

But it is said that when the Spanish conqueror of the ancient Incas demanded a room filled with golden gifts, the precious flask was among them. Whatever happened to this golden treasure is unknown, for the conqueror was killed and the Indians wandered over the mainland in search of a new leader. Some say the precious gifts—including the golden flask—are buried at the bottom of the lake at the end of the world, but no one besides Súmac has ever ventured to go there.

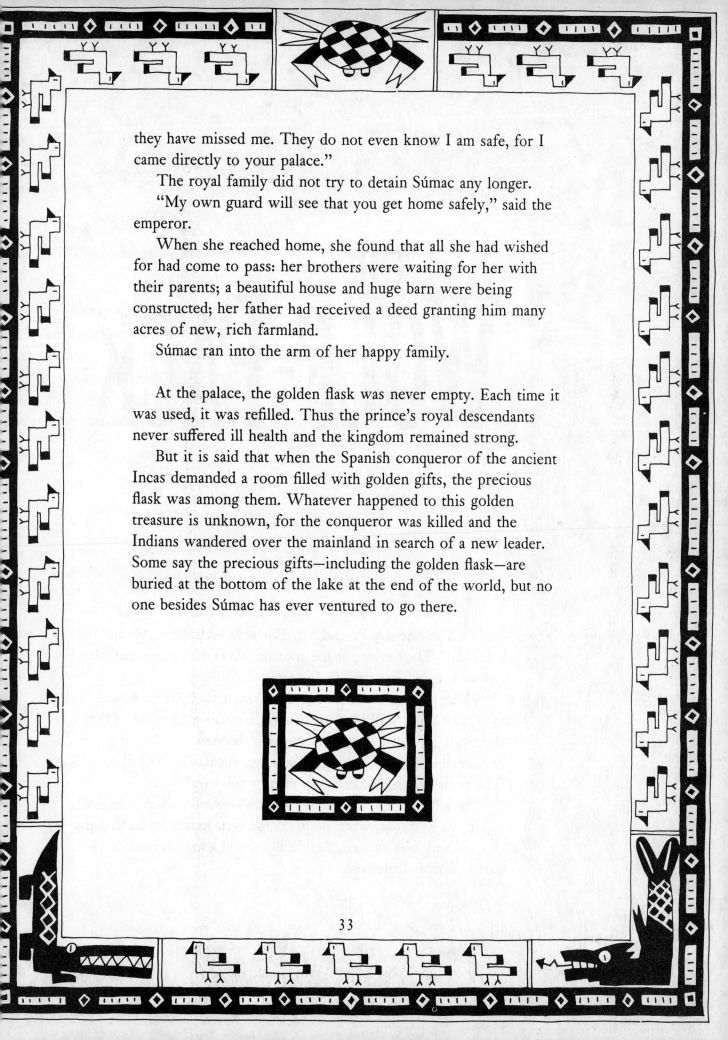

THE WOLF-PACK

a chapter from Little House on the Prairie
by Laura Ingalls Wilder

All in one day Pa and Mr. Edwards built the stable for Pet and Patty. They even put the roof on, working so late that Ma had to keep supper waiting for them.

There was no stable door, but in the moonlight Pa drove two stout posts well into the ground, one on either side of the doorway. He put Pet and Patty inside the stable, and then he laid small, split logs one above another, across the door space. The posts held them, and they made a solid wall.

"Now!" said Pa. "Let those wolves howl! I'll sleep, tonight."

In the morning, when he lifted the split logs from behind the posts, Laura was amazed. Beside Pet stood a long-legged, long-eared, wobbly little colt.

34

When Laura ran toward it, gentle Pet laid back her ears and snapped her teeth at Laura.

"Keep back, Laura!" Pa said, sharply. He said to Pet, "Now, Pet, you know we won't hurt your little colt." Pet answered him with a soft whinny. She would let Pa stroke her colt, but she would not let Laura or Mary come near it. When they even peeked at it through the cracks in the stable wall, Pet rolled the whites of her eyes at them and showed them her teeth. They had never seen a colt with ears so long. Pa said it was a little mule, but Laura said it looked like a jack rabbit. So they named the little colt Bunny.

When Pet was on the picket-line, with Bunny frisking around her and wondering at the big world, Laura must watch Baby Carrie carefully. If anyone but Pa came near Bunny, Pet squealed with rage and dashed to bite that little girl.

Early that Sunday afternoon Pa rode Patty away across the prairie to see what he should see. There was plenty of meat in the house, so he did not take his gun.

He rode away through the tall grass, along the rim of the creek bluffs. Birds flew up before him and circled and sank into the grasses. Pa was looking down into the creek bottoms as he rode; perhaps he was watching deer browsing there. Then Patty broke into a gallop, and swiftly she and Pa grew smaller. Soon there was only waving grass where they had been.

Late that afternoon Pa had not come home. Ma stirred the coals of the fire and laid chips on them, and began to get supper. Mary was in the house, minding the baby, and Laura asked Ma, "What's the matter with Jack?"

Jack was walking up and down, looking worried. He wrinkled his nose at the wind, and the hair rose up on his

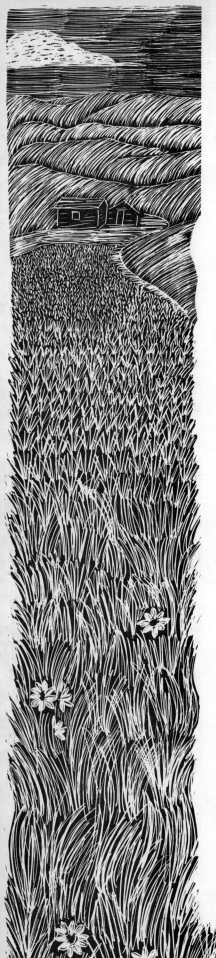

neck and lay down, and then rose up again. Pet's hoofs suddenly thudded. She ran around the circle of her picket-rope and stood still, whickering a low whicker. Bunny came close to her.

"What's the matter, Jack?" Ma asked. He looked up at her, but he couldn't say anything. Ma gazed around the whole circle of earth and sky. She could not see anything unusual.

"Likely it isn't anything, Laura," she said. She raked coals around the coffee-pot and the spider and onto the top of the bake oven. The prairie hen sizzled in the spider and the corncakes began to smell good. But all the time Ma kept glancing at the prairie all around. Jack walked about restlessly, and Pet did not graze. She faced the northwest, where Pa had gone, and kept her colt close beside her.

All at once Patty came running across the prairie. She was stretched out, running with all her might, and Pa was leaning almost flat on her neck.

She ran right past the stable before Pa could stop her. He stopped her so hard that she almost sat down. She was trembling all over and her black coat was streaked with sweat and foam. Pa swung off her. He was breathing hard, too.

"What is the matter, Charles?" Ma asked him.

Pa was looking toward the creek, so Ma and Laura looked at it, too. But they could see only the space above the bottom lands, with a few tree-tops in it, and the distant tops of the earthen bluffs under the High Prairie's grasses.

"What is it?" Ma asked again. "Why did you ride Patty like that?"

Pa breathed a long breath. "I was afraid the wolves would beat me here. But I see everything's all right."

"Wolves!" she cried. "What wolves?"

"Everything's all right, Caroline," said Pa. "Let a fellow get his breath."

When he had got some breath, he said, "I didn't ride Patty like that. It was all I could do to hold her at all. Fifty wolves, Caroline, the biggest wolves I ever saw. I wouldn't go through such a thing again, not for a mint of money."

A shadow came over the prairie just then because the sun had gone down, and Pa said, "I'll tell you about it later."

36

"We'll eat supper in the house," said Ma.

"No need of that," he told her. "Jack will give us warning in plenty of time."

He brought Pet and her colt from the picket-line. He didn't take them and Patty to drink from the creek, as he usually did. He gave them the water in Ma's washtub, which was standing full, ready for the washing next morning. He rubbed down Patty's sweaty sides and legs and put her in the barn with Pet and Bunny.

Supper was ready. The camp fire made a circle of light in the dark. Laura and Mary stayed close to the fire, and kept Baby Carrie with them. They could feel the dark all around them, and they kept looking behind them at the place where the dark mixed with the edge of the firelight. Shadows moved there, as if they were alive.

Jack sat on his haunches beside Laura. The edges of his ears were lifted, listening to the dark. Now and then he walked a little way into it. He walked all around the camp fire, and came back to sit beside Laura. The hair lay flat on his thick neck and he did not growl. His teeth showed a little, but that was because he was a bulldog.

Laura and Mary ate their corncakes and the prairie hen's drumsticks, and they listened to Pa while he told Ma about the wolves.

He had found some more neighbors. Settlers were coming in and settling along both sides of the creek. Less than three miles away, in a hollow on the High Prairie, a man and his wife were building a house. Their name was Scott, and Pa said they were nice folks. Six miles beyond them, two bachelors were living in one house. They had taken two farms, and built the house on the line between them. One man's bunk was against one wall of the house, and the other man's bunk was against the other wall. So each man slept on his own farm, although they were in the same house and the house was only eight feet wide. They cooked and ate together in the middle of the house.

Pa had not said anything about the wolves yet. Laura wished he would. But she knew that she must not interrupt when Pa was talking.

37

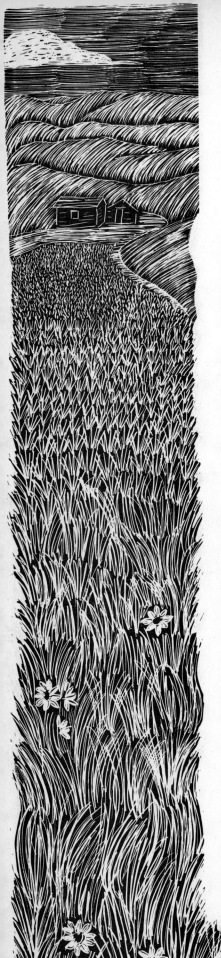

He said that these bachelors did not know that anyone else was in the country. They had seen nobody but Indians. So they were glad to see Pa, and he stayed there longer than he had meant to.

Then he rode on, and from a little rise in the prairie he saw a white speck down in the creek bottoms. He thought it was a covered wagon, and it was. When he came to it, he found a man and his wife and five children. They had come from Iowa, and they had camped in the bottoms because one of their horses was sick. The horse was better now, but the bad night air so near the creek had given them fever 'n' ague. The man and his wife and the three oldest children were too sick to stand up. The little boy and girl, no bigger than Mary and Laura, were taking care of them.

So Pa did what he could for them, and then he rode back to tell the bachelors about them. One of them rode right away to fetch that family up on the High Prairie, where they would soon get well in the good air.

One thing had led to another, until Pa was starting home later than he had meant. He took a short cut across the prairie, and as he was loping along on Patty, suddenly out of a little draw came a pack of wolves. They were all around Pa in a moment.

"It was a big pack," Pa said. "All of fifty wolves, and the biggest wolves I ever saw in my life. Must be what they call buffalo wolves. Their leader's a big gray brute that stands three feet at the shoulder, if an inch. I tell you my hair stood straight on end."

"And you didn't have your gun," said Ma.

"I thought of that. But my gun would have been no use if I'd had it. You can't fight fifty wolves with one gun. And Patty couldn't outrun them."

"What did you do?" Ma asked.

"Nothing," said Pa. "Patty tried to run. I never wanted anything worse than I wanted to get away from there. But I knew if Patty even started, those wolves would be on us in a minute, pulling us down. So I held Patty to a walk."

"Goodness, Charles!" Ma said under her breath.

"Yes. I wouldn't go through such a thing again for any money. Caroline, I never saw such wolves. One big fellow trotted along, right by my stirrup. I could have kicked him in the ribs. They didn't pay any attention to me at all. They must have just made a kill and eaten all they could.

"I tell you, Caroline, those wolves just closed in around Patty and me and trotted along with us. In broad daylight. For all the world like a pack of dogs going along with a horse. They were all around us, trotting along, and jumping and playing and snapping at each other, just like dogs."

"Goodness, Charles!" Ma said again. Laura's heart was thumping fast, and her mouth and her eyes were wide open, staring at Pa.

"Patty was shaking all over, and fighting the bit," said Pa. "Sweat ran off her, she was so scared. I was sweating, too. But I held her down to a walk, and we went walking along among those wolves. They came right along with us, a quarter of a mile or more. That big fellow trotted by my stirrup as if he were there to stay.

"Then we came to the head of a draw, running down into the creek bottoms. The big gray leader went down it, and all the rest of the pack trotted down into it, behind him. As soon as the last one was in the draw, I let Patty go.

"She headed straight for home, across the prairie. And she couldn't have run faster if I'd been cutting into her with a rawhide whip. I was scared the whole way. I thought the wolves might be coming this way and they might be making better time than I was. I was glad you had the gun, Caroline. And glad the house is built. I knew you could keep the wolves out of the house, with the gun. But Pet and the colt were outside."

"You need not have worried, Charles," Ma said. "I guess I would manage to save our horses."

"I was not fully reasonable, at the time," said Pa. "I know you would save the horses, Caroline. Those wolves wouldn't bother you, anyway. If they had been hungry, I wouldn't be here to—"

"Little pitchers have big ears," Ma said. She meant that he must not frighten Mary and Laura.

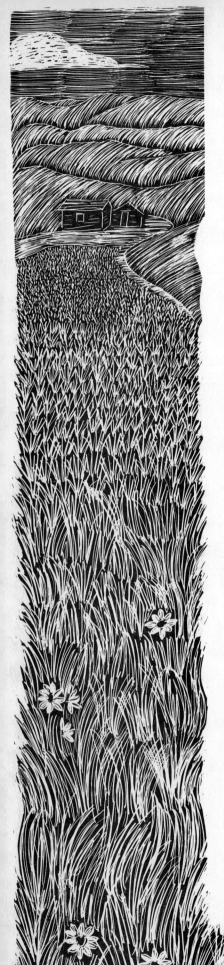

"Well, all's well that ends well," Pa replied. "And those wolves are miles from here by now."

"What made them act like that?" Laura asked him.

"I don't know, Laura," he said. "I guess they had just eaten all they could hold, and they were on their way to the creek to get a drink. Or perhaps they were out playing on the prairie, and not paying any attention to anything but their play, like little girls do sometimes. Perhaps they saw that I didn't have my gun and couldn't do them any harm. Or perhaps they had never seen a man before and didn't know that men can do them any harm. So they didn't think about me at all."

Pet and Patty were restlessly walking around and around, inside the barn. Jack walked around the camp fire. When he stood still to smell the air and listen, the hair lifted on his neck.

"Bedtime for little girls!" Ma said, cheerfully. Not even Baby Carrie was sleepy yet, but Ma took them all into the house. She told Mary and Laura to go to bed, and she put Baby Carrie's little nightgown on and laid her in the big bed. Then she went outdoors to do the dishes. Laura wanted Pa and Ma in the house. They seemed so far away outside.

Mary and Laura were good and lay still, but Carrie sat up and played by herself in the dark. In the dark Pa's arm came from behind the quilt in the doorway and quietly took away his gun. Out by the camp fire the tin plates rattled. Then a knife scraped the spider. Ma and Pa were talking together and Laura smelled tobacco smoke.

The house was safe, but it did not feel safe because Pa's gun was not over the door and there was no door; there was only the quilt.

After a long time Ma lifted the quilt. Baby Carrie was asleep then. Ma and Pa came in very quietly and very quietly went to bed. Jack lay across the doorway, but his chin was not on his paws. His head was up, listening. Ma breathed softly, Pa breathed heavily, and Mary was asleep, too. But Laura strained her eyes in the dark to watch Jack. She could not tell whether the hair was standing up on his neck.

Suddenly she was sitting straight up in bed. She had been asleep. The dark was gone. Moonlight streamed through the window hole and streaks of moonlight came through every crack in that wall. Pa stood black in the moonlight at the window. He had his gun.

Right in Laura's ear a wolf howled.

She scringed away from the wall. The wolf was on the other side of it. Laura was too scared to make a sound. The cold was not in her backbone only, it was all through her. Mary pulled the quilt over her head. Jack growled and showed his teeth at the quilt in the doorway.

"Be still, Jack," Pa said.

Terrible howls curled all around inside the house, and Laura rose out of bed. She wanted to go to Pa, but she knew better than to bother him now. He turned his head and saw her standing in her nightgown.

"Want to see them, Laura?" he asked, softly. Laura couldn't say anything, but she nodded, and padded across the ground to him. He stood his gun against the wall and lifted her up to the window hole.

There in the moonlight sat half a circle of wolves. They sat on their haunches and looked at Laura in the window, and she looked at them. She had never seen such big wolves. The biggest one was taller than Laura. He was taller even than Mary. He sat in the middle, exactly opposite Laura. Everything about him was big—his pointed ears, and his pointed mouth with the tongue hanging out, and his strong shoulders and legs, and his two paws side by side, and his tail curled around the squatting haunch. His coat was shaggy gray and his eyes were glittering green.

Laura clutched her toes into a crack of the wall and she folded her arms on the window slab, and she looked and looked at that wolf. But she did not put her head through the empty window space into the outdoors where all those wolves sat so near her, shifting their paws and licking their chops. Pa stood firm against her back and kept his arm tight around her middle.

"He's awful big," Laura whispered.

"Yes, and see how his coat shines," Pa whispered into her hair. The moonlight made little glitters in the edges of the shaggy fur, all around the big wolf.

41

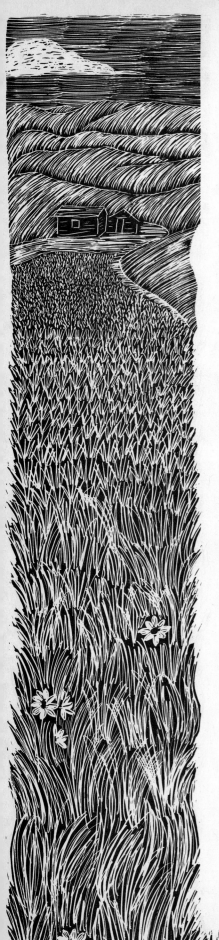

"They are in a ring clear around the house," Pa whispered. Laura pattered beside him to the other window. He leaned his gun against that wall and lifted her up again. There, sure enough, was the other half of the circle of wolves. All their eyes glittered green in the shadow of the house. Laura could hear their breathing. When they saw Pa and Laura looking out, the middle of the circle moved back a little way.

Pet and Patty were squealing and running inside the barn. Their hoofs pounded the ground and crashed against the walls.

After a moment Pa went back to the other window, and Laura went, too. They were just in time to see the big wolf lift his nose till it pointed straight at the sky. His mouth opened, and a long howl rose toward the moon.

Then all around the house the circle of wolves pointed their noses toward the sky and answered him. Their howls shuddered through the house and filled the moonlight and quavered away across the vast silence of the prairie.

"Now go back to bed, little half-pint," Pa said. "Go to sleep. Jack and I will take care of you all."

So Laura went back to bed. But for a long time she did not sleep. She lay and listened to the breathing of the wolves on the other side of the log wall. She heard the scratch of their claws on the ground, and the snuffling of a nose at a crack. She heard the big gray leader howl again, and all the others answering him.

But Pa was walking quietly from one window hole to the other, and Jack did not stop pacing up and down before the quilt that hung in the doorway. The wolves might howl, but they could not get in while Pa and Jack were there. So at last Laura fell asleep.

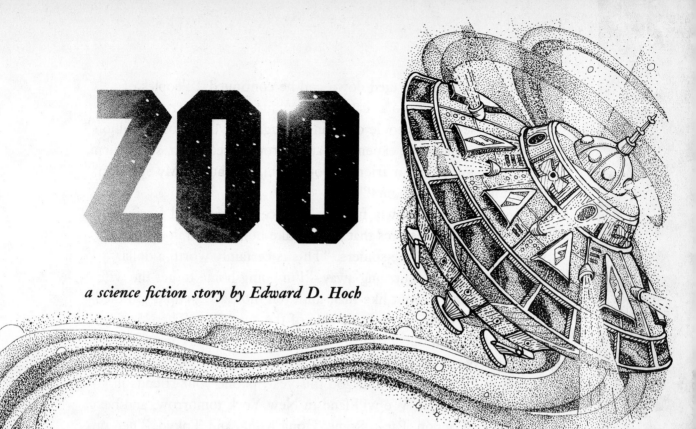

ZOO

a science fiction story by Edward D. Hoch

The children were always good during the month of August, especially when it began to get near the twenty-third. It was on this day that the great silver spaceship carrying Professor Hugo's Interplanetary Zoo settled down for its annual six-hour visit to the Chicago area.

Before daybreak the crowds would form, long lines of children and adults both, each one clutching his or her dollar, and waiting with wonderment to see what race of strange creatures the Professor had brought this year.

In the past they had sometimes been treated to three-legged creatures from Venus, or tall, thin men from Mars, or even snakelike horrors from somewhere more distant. This year, as the great round ship settled slowly to earth in the huge tri-city parking area just outside of Chicago, they watched with awe as the sides slowly slid up to reveal the familiar barred cages. In them were some wild breed of nightmare—small, horselike animals that moved with quick, jerking motions and constantly chattered in a high-pitched tongue. The citizens of Earth clustered around as Professor Hugo's crew quickly collected the waiting dollars, and soon the good Professor himself made an appearance, wearing his many-colored rainbow cape and top hat. "Peoples of Earth," he called into his microphone.

The crowd's noise died down and he continued. "Peoples of Earth, this year you see a real treat for your single dollar—the little-known horse-spider people of Kaan—brought to you across a million miles of space at great expense. Gather around, see them, study them, listen to them, tell your friends about them. But hurry! My ship can remain here only six hours!"

And the crowds slowly filed by, at once horrified and fascinated by these strange creatures that looked like horses but ran up the walls of their cages like spiders. "This is certainly worth a dollar," one man remarked, hurrying away. "I'm going home to get the wife."

All day long it went like that, until ten thousand people had filed by the barred cages set into the side of the spaceship. Then, as the six-hour limit ran out, Professor Hugo once more took microphone in hand. "We must go now, but we will return next year on this date. And if you enjoyed our zoo this year, phone your friends in other cities about it. We will land in New York tomorrow, and next week on to London, Paris, Rome, Hong Kong, and Tokyo. Then on to other worlds!"

He waved farewell to them, and as the ship rose from the ground the Earth peoples agreed that this had been the very best Zoo yet. . . .

Some two months and three planets later, the silver ship of Professor Hugo settled at last onto the familiar jagged rocks of Kaan, and the queer horse-spider creatures filed quickly out of their cages. Professor Hugo was there to say a few parting words, and then they scurried away in a hundred different directions, seeking their homes among the rocks.

In one, the she-creature was happy to see the return of her mate and offspring. She babbled a greeting in the strange tongue and hurried to embrace them. "It was a long time you were gone. Was it good?"

And the he-creature nodded. "The little one enjoyed it especially. We visited eight worlds and saw many things."

The little one ran up the wall of the cave. "On the place called earth it was the best. The creatures there wear garments over their skins, and they walk on two legs."

"But isn't it dangerous?" asked the she-creature.

"No," her mate answered. "There are bars to protect us from them. We remain right in the ship. Next time you must come with us. It is well worth the nineteen commocs it costs."

And the little one nodded. "It was the very best Zoo ever. . . ."

Why Bear Sleeps All Winter

a black American folk tale
by Maria Leach

In the first days of the world, Bear stayed awake all winter just like any other animal.

All the animals thought he was a mean old thing. He was the biggest, so he always had his own way, and the other animals felt put upon. They all felt pretty mad at Old Man Bear a lot of the time.

They called a big meeting one day. All the animals came together to discuss what they could do about Old Man Bear. The meeting went on and on for many days, because nobody could think of what to do.

Then one day Rabbit suddenly remembered that Bear liked to curl up and sleep in a dark, hollow tree.

"Next time let's stop up the tree!" said Rabbit.

All the animals were delighted with this idea. "Maybe he'll take a long nap," they said, "and we'll get some rest."

So they kept watch on Old Man Bear. That night when Bear crawled into a hollow tree to go to sleep, they all worked hard. Everybody brought rocks and boughs and brush and more rocks to stop up the hole in the tree.

In the morning Bear woke up. It was dark in there. He said, "Sun not up yet," and turned over and went to sleep again. This time he slept on and on in the warm place till spring came and little leaves were unfolding on the trees.

"Do you suppose he's dead?" the animals said to each other. "Didn't he wake up at all?"

Curiosity got the better of them. They had to go peek. So they moved away the rocks and looked in.

There was Old Man Bear sound asleep. When the sunlight poured in on his face, he opened his eyes to little slits and blinked. He stretched; and when he looked and saw the leaves on the trees he got up and came out in the sun.

"The comfortablest winter I ever had!" said Bear.

Now every year Bear finds a nice warm secret place and curls up and sleeps all winter.

The Contest

a story from the Dan people of Liberia
told by Won-Ldy Paye

Once upon a time, way out in the village, lived a man called Spider. Sometimes they called Spider "Anansi." Spider was a great dancer. Spider used to travel all around the world. Everybody knew about Spider because Spider could DANCE! Spider was the greatest dancer in the WHOLE WORLD!

Now there were two forest monsters who lived way out in the mountains. They were really ugly. They were jealous of Spider because people said he was such a great dancer, and they said to one another, "Why does everybody in the village think that Spider is a great dancer? We don't like that idea. We will go to the village and show the people that we can dance, too."

They sat down and started thinking. One forest monster said, "How can we get the people in the village to watch us dance? We are so ugly that all the people will run away from us."

47

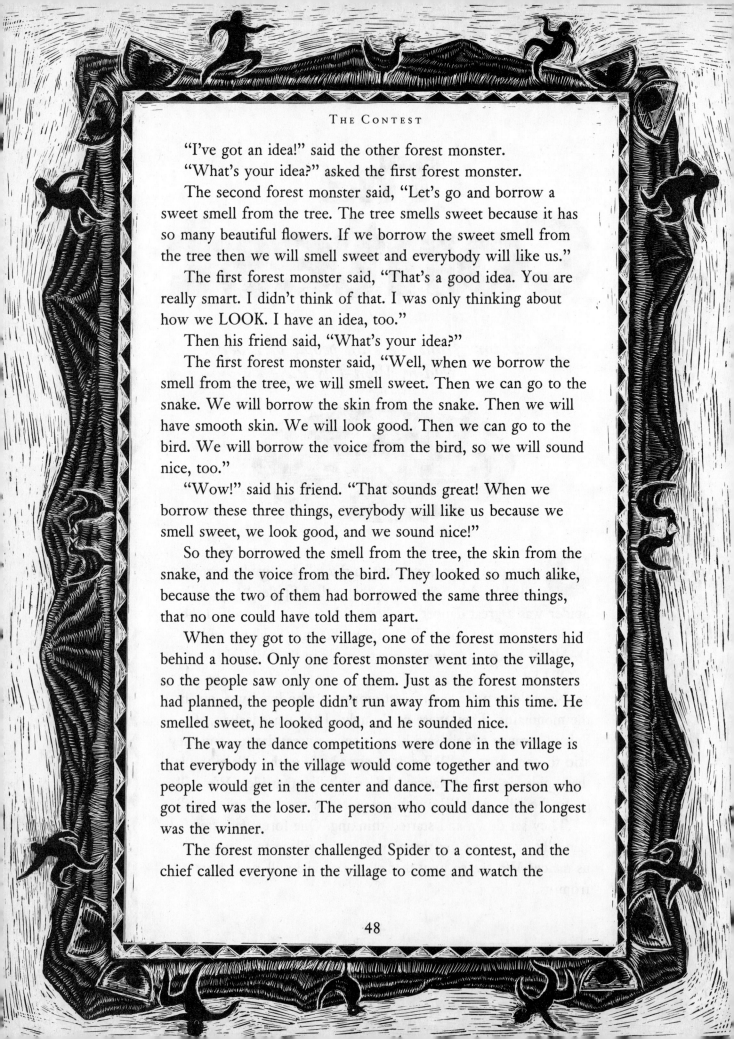

"I've got an idea!" said the other forest monster.

"What's your idea?" asked the first forest monster.

The second forest monster said, "Let's go and borrow a sweet smell from the tree. The tree smells sweet because it has so many beautiful flowers. If we borrow the sweet smell from the tree then we will smell sweet and everybody will like us."

The first forest monster said, "That's a good idea. You are really smart. I didn't think of that. I was only thinking about how we LOOK. I have an idea, too."

Then his friend said, "What's your idea?"

The first forest monster said, "Well, when we borrow the smell from the tree, we will smell sweet. Then we can go to the snake. We will borrow the skin from the snake. Then we will have smooth skin. We will look good. Then we can go to the bird. We will borrow the voice from the bird, so we will sound nice, too."

"Wow!" said his friend. "That sounds great! When we borrow these three things, everybody will like us because we smell sweet, we look good, and we sound nice!"

So they borrowed the smell from the tree, the skin from the snake, and the voice from the bird. They looked so much alike, because the two of them had borrowed the same three things, that no one could have told them apart.

When they got to the village, one of the forest monsters hid behind a house. Only one forest monster went into the village, so the people saw only one of them. Just as the forest monsters had planned, the people didn't run away from him this time. He smelled sweet, he looked good, and he sounded nice.

The way the dance competitions were done in the village is that everybody in the village would come together and two people would get in the center and dance. The first person who got tired was the loser. The person who could dance the longest was the winner.

The forest monster challenged Spider to a contest, and the chief called everyone in the village to come and watch the contest. Everybody came to watch. They all started to sing:

> "Glay-guhn ga nuann day,
>   Nann per tea.
> Glay-guhn ga nuann day-ay,
>   Nann per tea."

> [Here comes the forest monster,
>   Little children.
> Here comes the forest monster,
>   Little children.]

Some of the people had drums, and they drummed to the beat of the singing. The music echoed throughout the village.

Spider and the forest monster started dancing. They danced, and they danced, and they danced. Everybody was saying, "Wow! This forest monster can dance!"

They started dancing all over the place. They were dancing, and dancing, and dancing. Everybody was saying, "This is a great dance contest!"

Finally the forest monster started getting tired. When the forest monster got too tired, he slowly danced around behind the house. The people didn't know what was behind the house. They thought he was just having fun dancing all over the place. But the forest monster was really switching with the other forest monster who was there.

The second forest monster came out from behind the house, dancing. Because he hadn't been dancing all the time, he had lots of energy.

The people kept drumming and singing:

> "Glay-guhn ga nuann day,
>   Nann per tea.
> Glay-guhn ga nuann day-ay,
>   Nann per tea."

Spider and the forest monster danced, and they danced, and they danced. They were doing all their best moves. People in

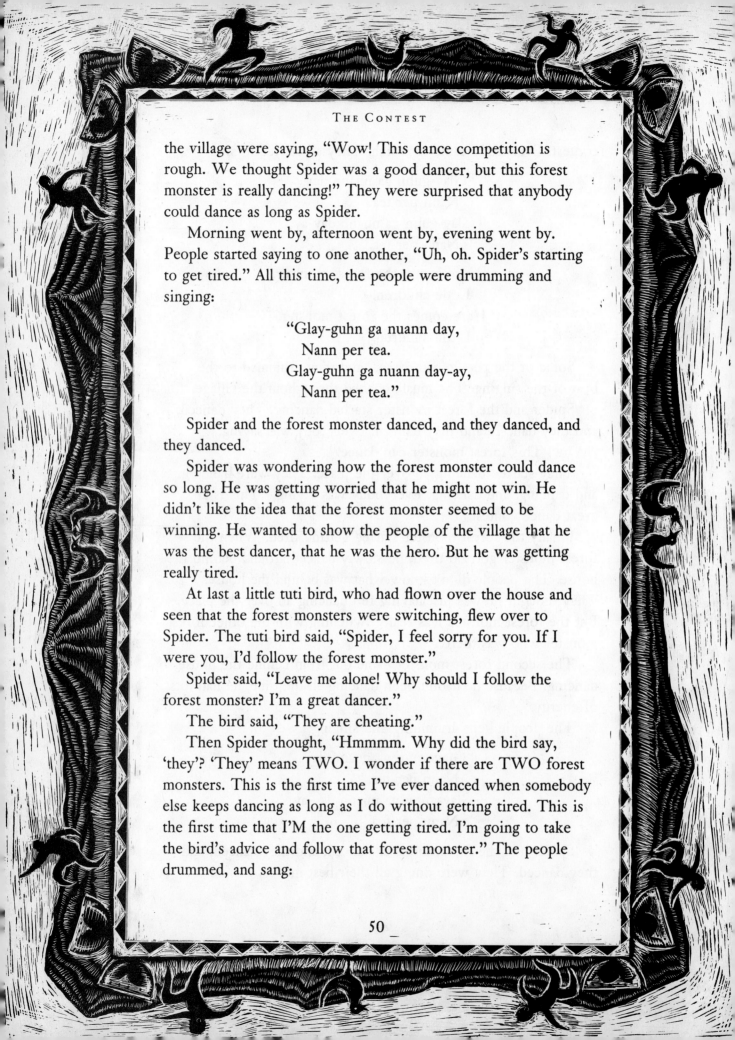

the village were saying, "Wow! This dance competition is rough. We thought Spider was a good dancer, but this forest monster is really dancing!" They were surprised that anybody could dance as long as Spider.

Morning went by, afternoon went by, evening went by. People started saying to one another, "Uh, oh. Spider's starting to get tired." All this time, the people were drumming and singing:

"Glay-guhn ga nuann day,
    Nann per tea.
Glay-guhn ga nuann day-ay,
    Nann per tea."

Spider and the forest monster danced, and they danced, and they danced.

Spider was wondering how the forest monster could dance so long. He was getting worried that he might not win. He didn't like the idea that the forest monster seemed to be winning. He wanted to show the people of the village that he was the best dancer, that he was the hero. But he was getting really tired.

At last a little tuti bird, who had flown over the house and seen that the forest monsters were switching, flew over to Spider. The tuti bird said, "Spider, I feel sorry for you. If I were you, I'd follow the forest monster."

Spider said, "Leave me alone! Why should I follow the forest monster? I'm a great dancer."

The bird said, "They are cheating."

Then Spider thought, "Hmmmm. Why did the bird say, 'they'? 'They' means TWO. I wonder if there are TWO forest monsters. This is the first time I've ever danced when somebody else keeps dancing as long as I do without getting tired. This is the first time that I'M the one getting tired. I'm going to take the bird's advice and follow that forest monster." The people drummed, and sang:

"Glay-guhn ga nuann day,
  Nann per tea.
Glay-guhn ga nuann day-ay,
  Nann per tea."

Spider followed the forest monster. They started dancing all over the place. Everywhere that the forest monster was dancing, Spider followed him. The forest monster was getting tired. He was ready to switch again with his friend. He started going behind the house, but he could see that Spider was following him all around now. The forest monster wanted to cheat, but he couldn't go behind the house and switch with the other forest monster because Spider would follow and catch him cheating. So the forest monster had to turn around because he didn't want Spider to see the other forest monster behind the house.

The forest monster's feet were getting tired. The people could see that he was getting tired, but they kept drumming and singing:

"Glay-guhn ga nuann day,
  Nann per tea.
Glay-guhn ga nuann day-ay,
  Nann per tea."

The forest monster danced slower and slower. He was tired.

He got on his knees and danced on his knees. His knees got tired.

He got on his stomach and danced on his stomach. His stomach got tired.

He danced on his back, and his back got tired.

He danced on his shoulders, and his shoulders got tired.

He danced on his hands, and his hands got tired.

He even tried to dance on his head—BOOM! He fell down.

Spider had a big smile on his face. He was HAPPY! He was dancing all over the place. At last the people could stop singing

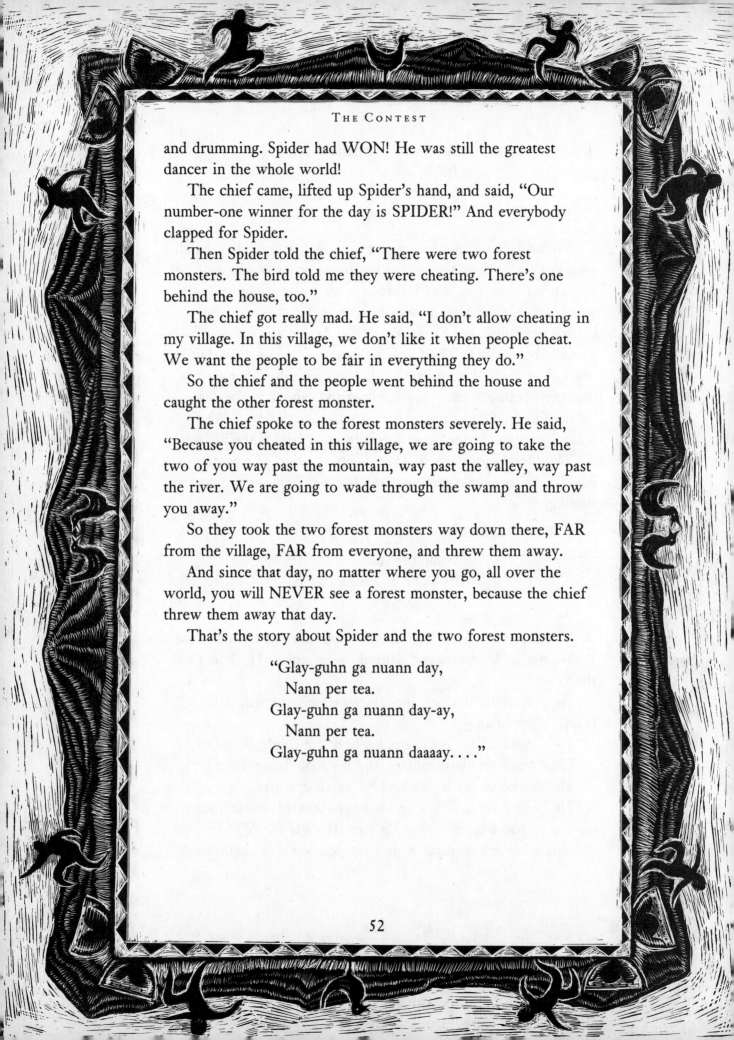

and drumming. Spider had WON! He was still the greatest dancer in the whole world!

The chief came, lifted up Spider's hand, and said, "Our number-one winner for the day is SPIDER!" And everybody clapped for Spider.

Then Spider told the chief, "There were two forest monsters. The bird told me they were cheating. There's one behind the house, too."

The chief got really mad. He said, "I don't allow cheating in my village. In this village, we don't like it when people cheat. We want the people to be fair in everything they do."

So the chief and the people went behind the house and caught the other forest monster.

The chief spoke to the forest monsters severely. He said, "Because you cheated in this village, we are going to take the two of you way past the mountain, way past the valley, way past the river. We are going to wade through the swamp and throw you away."

So they took the two forest monsters way down there, FAR from the village, FAR from everyone, and threw them away.

And since that day, no matter where you go, all over the world, you will NEVER see a forest monster, because the chief threw them away that day.

That's the story about Spider and the two forest monsters.

> "Glay-guhn ga nuann day,
>   Nann per tea.
> Glay-guhn ga nuann day-ay,
>   Nann per tea.
> Glay-guhn ga nuann daaaay. . . ."

THE
SEA OF
GOLD

*a Japanese folk tale
adapted by Yoshiko
Uchida*

On a small island, where almost every able bodied man was a fisherman, there once lived a young man named Hikoichi. He was gentle and kind, but he was not very bright, and there was no one on the whole island who was willing to teach him how to become a fisherman.

"How could we ever make a fisherman out of you?" people would say to him. "You are much too slow to learn anything!"

But Hikoichi wanted very badly to go to work, and he tried hard to find a job. He looked and looked for many months until finally he found work as cook on one of the fishing boats. He got the job, however, only because no one else wanted it. No one wanted to work in a hot steaming galley, cooking rice and chopping vegetables, while the boat pitched and rolled in the middle of the sea. No one wanted to be the cook who always got the smallest share of the boat's catch. But Hikoichi didn't mind at all. He was happy to have any kind of job at last.

The fishermen on his boat liked to tease him and they would often call him Slowpoke or Stupid. "Get busy and make us something decent to eat, Stupid!" they would shout to him. Or, "The rice is only half-cooked, Slowpoke!" they would complain.

But no matter how they shouted or what they called him, Hikoichi never grew angry. He only answered, "Yes sir," or "I'm sorry, sir," and that was all.

Hikoichi was very careful with the food he cooked, and he tried not to waste even a single grain of rice. In fact, he hated to throw away any of the leftovers, and he stored them carefully in the galley cupboards. On the

53

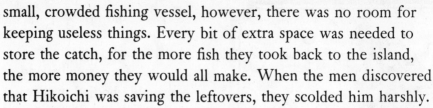

small, crowded fishing vessel, however, there was no room for keeping useless things. Every bit of extra space was needed to store the catch, for the more fish they took back to the island, the more money they would all make. When the men discovered that Hikoichi was saving the leftovers, they scolded him harshly.

"Stupid fool!" they shouted. "Don't use our valuable space for storing garbage. Throw it into the sea!"

"What a terrible waste of good food," Hikoichi thought, but he had to do as he was told. He gathered up all the leftovers he had stored and took them up on deck.

"If I must throw this into the sea," he said to himself, "I will make sure the fish have a good feast. After all, if it were not for the fish, we wouldn't be able to make a living." And so, as he threw the leftovers into the water, he called out, "Here fish, here, good fish, have yourselves a splendid dinner!"

From that day, Hikoichi always called to the fish before he threw his leftovers into the sea. "*Sab sab*, come along," he would call. "Enjoy some rice from my galley!" And he continued talking to them until they had devoured every morsel he tossed overboard.

The fishermen laughed when they heard him. "Listen to the young fool talking to the fish," they jeered. And to Hikoichi they said, "Maybe someday they will answer you and tell you how much they enjoyed your dinner."

But Hikoichi didn't pay any attention to the fishermen. He silently gathered all the scraps from the table and continued to toss them out to the fish at the end of the day. Each time he did, he called to the fish as though they were his best friends, and his gentle voice echoed far out over the dancing waves of the sea.

In such a fashion, many years went by until Hikoichi was no longer a young man. He continued to cook for the men on his fishing boat, however, and he still fed and talked to the fish every evening.

One day, the fishing boat put far out to sea in search of bigger fish. It sailed for three days and three nights, going farther and farther away from the small island. On the third night, they were still far out at sea when they dropped anchor. It was a quiet star-filled night with a full moon glowing high in the sky. The men were tired from the day's work and not long after dinner, they were all sound asleep.

Hikoichi, however, still had much to do. He scrubbed the pots, cleaned up his galley and washed the rice for breakfast. When he had finished, he gathered all the leftovers in a basket and went up on deck.

"Gather around, good fish," he called as always. "Enjoy your dinner."

He emptied his basket and stayed to watch the fish eat up his food. Then, he went to his bunk to prepare for bed, but somehow the boat felt very peculiar. It had stopped rolling. In fact, it was not moving at all and felt as though it were standing on dry land.

"That's odd," Hikoichi thought, and he ran up on deck to see what had happened. He leaned over the rail and looked out.

"What!" he shouted. "The ocean is gone!"

And indeed it had disappeared. There was not a single drop of water anywhere. As far as Hikoichi could see, there was nothing but miles and miles of sand. It was as though the boat were standing in the middle of a vast desert of shimmering sand.

"What has happened?" Hikoichi wondered. "Have we suddenly beached ourselves on an unknown island? Did the ocean dry up? But no, that is impossible. I must be dreaming!"

Hikoichi blinked hard and shook his head. Then he pinched himself on the cheek, but he was not dreaming. Hikoichi was alarmed. He wanted to go below to wake the others, but he knew they would be very angry to be awakened in the middle of the night. They would shout at him and call him a stupid fool and tell him he was out of his mind. Hikoichi decided he wouldn't awaken them after all. If the boat was still on land in the morning, the men would see for themselves.

Hikoichi could not believe his eyes. He simply had to get off the boat to see if they really were standing on dry land. Slowly, he lowered himself down a rope ladder and reached the sand below. Carefully, he took a step and felt his foot crunch on something solid. No, it wasn't water. It really was sand after all. Hikoichi blinked as he looked around, for under the light of the moon, the sand glittered and sparkled like a beach of gold. He

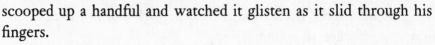

scooped up a handful and watched it glisten as it slid through his fingers.

"Why, this is beautiful," Hikoichi thought, and his heart sang with joy at the splendor of the sight. "I must save some of this sand so I can remember this wonderful night forever." He hurried back onto the boat for a bucket, filled it with the sparkling sand and then carried it aboard and hid it carefully beneath his bunk. He looked around at the other men, but they were all sound asleep. Not one seemed to have noticed that the boat was standing still. Hikoichi slipped quietly into his narrow, dark bunk, and soon he too was sound asleep.

The next morning Hikoichi was the first to wake up. He remembered the remarkable happening of the night before, and he leaped out of bed, ready to call the other men to see the strange sight. But as he got dressed, he felt the familiar rocking of the boat. He hurried up on deck and he saw that once again they were out in the middle of the ocean with waves all about them. Hikoichi shook his head, but now he could no longer keep it all to himself. As soon as the other men came up on deck, he told his story.

"It's true," he cried as he saw wide grins appear on the men's faces. "The ocean was gone and for miles and miles there was nothing but sand. It glittered and sparkled under the full moon and it was as though we were sailing on a sea of golden sand!"

The men roared with laughter. "Hikoichi, you were surely drunk," they said. "Now put away your daydreams and fix us some breakfast."

"No, no, I wasn't drunk and I wasn't dreaming," Hikoichi insisted. "I climbed down the ladder and I walked on the sand. I picked it up and felt it slip through my fingers. It wasn't a dream. It really wasn't."

"Poor old Slowpoke," the men sneered. "Your brain has finally become addled. We will have to send you home."

It was then that Hikoichi remembered his bucket. "Wait! Come with me and I can prove it," he said, and he led the men down to his bunk. Then, getting down on his hands and knees, he carefully pulled out his bucket of sand.

"There!" he said proudly. "I scooped this up when I went down and walked on the sand. Now do you believe me?"

The men suddenly stopped laughing. "This isn't sand," they said, reaching out to feel it. "It's gold! It's a bucket full of pure gold!"

"Why didn't you get more, you poor fool?" one of the men shouted.

"You've got to give some of it to us," another added.

"We share our fish with you. You must share your gold with us," said still another.

Soon all the men were yelling and shouting and pushing to get their hands on Hikoichi's bucket of gold.

Then the oldest of the fishermen spoke up. "Stop it! Stop it!" he called out. "This gold doesn't belong to any of you. It belongs to Hikoichi."

He reminded the men how Hikoichi had fed the fish of the sea for so many years as though they were his own children.

"Now the King of the Sea has given Hikoichi a reward for his kindness to the fish," he explained. And turning to Hikoichi, he added, "You are not stupid or a fool or a slowpoke, my friend. You are gentle and kind and good. This gift from the Kingdom of the Sea is your reward. Take all the gold and keep it, for it belongs only to you."

The shouting, pushing fishermen suddenly became silent and thoughtful, for they knew the old fisherman was right. They were ashamed of having laughed at Hikoichi year after year, and they knew that he truly deserved this fine reward.

Without another word the men went back to work. They completed their catch that day and the heavily laden boat returned once more to the little island.

The next time the boat put out to sea, Hikoichi was no longer aboard, for now he had enough gold to leave his job as cook forever. He built himself a beautiful new house, and he even had a small boat of his own so he could still sail out to sea and feed the fish. He used his treasure from the sea wisely and well, and he lived a long and happy life on the little island where no one ever called him Stupid or Slowpoke again.

The Lion and the Mouse

a fable by Aesop
retold by Margaret H. Lippert

Once, long ago, a lion lay asleep in his lair. A tiny mouse looking for food entered the cave and scurried across the floor. Because it was dark in the cave, he couldn't see the lion in his way. The mouse ran over to the lion's foot, and the lion woke up.

The frightened mouse tried to escape, but the lion moved swiftly. He caught the mouse with his paw, and lifted the mouse toward his open jaws. "You will be a tender morsel," roared the lion.

"Don't eat me," pleaded the mouse. "If you let me go I will repay your kindness some day."

"YOU?" roared the lion. "How could a little creature like you help a mighty beast like me?"

"Let me go, and you will see," replied the mouse. The lion was amused by the idea that the little mouse could help him, so he let the mouse go. The mouse ran out of the cave to the safety of his burrow, and the lion went back to sleep.

Many days passed. Then one morning the lion was roaming through the forest. Suddenly he found himself trapped in a net laid by some hunters. He struggled to get free, but as he struggled, the net tightened around him. Soon he could move no more. He lay helplessly in the net.

In terror the lion roared. His desperate roars echoed throughout the forest. The little mouse recognized the voice of the lion who had freed him, and came running to see what was wrong.

When the mouse saw the lion trapped in the net, he knew that he could help the lion. At once the mouse set to work. He gnawed the ropes that bound the lion, and one after another the ropes fell apart. Before long the mouse had made a hole in the net big enough for the lion to squeeze through.

The lion crept out of the hole and turned to the mouse. "You have saved my life," he told the mouse. "I had given up all hope. I thought I would surely die. But you, a tiny mouse, have set me free."

"You see, I was right," responded the mouse. "A little friend can be a big help."

PECOS BILL INVENTS THE LARIAT

a tall tale from Texas by James Cloyd Bowman

All the men of the I. X. L. were eating out of Pecos Bill's hand within less than a week after he arrived. He took to the life of a cowboy like a duck to water. He learned their best tricks, then went on to do better. Gun Smith and Chuck and the rest were very soon like children before him. Among themselves, they bragged about their noble deeds; but when Pecos was around, they couldn't help thinking that they were mere bridled cayuses.

He could stand on the ground beside a broncho, turn an air flop, and land astride the pony before it had time to tighten a muscle. He could ride bareback without a bridle. He could urge his pony at top speed over ground so rough and uneven that Gun Smith and the others were afraid even to attempt it with bit and saddle. And he was so casual and modest about everything he did that they thought Pecos the eighth wonder of the world. Almost at once he was full of ideas. And what ideas!

Up to Pecos Bill's day, when a man wanted to capture a horse or a steer, he would lay a piece of rope down on the ground, make a loop in one end of it, sit down behind a tree or a blind, and by laying a bait, try to coax the wild critter to step within the loop. He would then jerk sharply on the rope, and perhaps one time in a dozen, if he was lucky, he would succeed in making a catch. It was no uncommon thing for a man to wait around and lose an entire month's time without laying hold of a single animal.

"Well, this sort of thing has got to be changed," said Pecos Bill to himself when no one was near to hear him. "A man can't be expected to waste his entire lifetime catching a single horse or cow."

Without further delay, Pecos got hold of the longest piece of rope he could find around the ranch, and began to throw it through the air. Next he rode off alone where the others could not see what he was doing. After three days of constant practice, he found that he could lasso almost anything. He was limited only by the reach of his line.

Pecos Bill would just make a large loop in one end of his rope, swing it wildly about his head three or four times, and then, with a quick flip of his forearm and wrist, send it flying like a bullet. And as he grew more and more skilled, he added rapidly to the length of his rope.

As soon as he was entirely sure of himself, Pecos asked the boys to come out and let him show them his new invention.

"See that roan steer across there? That's Old Crook-horn, our wildest critter, ain't it?" Pecos asked quietly.

Before anyone was aware of what he was doing, Pecos had whirled his loop about his head and had sent it so fast in the direction of the four-year-old, that the eye could scarcely follow it.

In an instant the old steer began to jump and bellow, and Pecos Bill to tow in the rope. Soon the astonished steer stood with lowered head before the even more surprised cowboys.

Not content with this great skill, Pecos began practicing from horseback.

In another week, he again called his cowboys out to see what he could do. They watched, with popping eyes, as he gave his rope a double turn around his saddle-bow. He then started his broncho at a hard gallop. They saw him quickly approach a rather tall, scraggly mesquite tree, whirl his loop wildly about his head and then fling it into the air. When he dragged a great hawk down from the topmost branch with the noose about its neck, the men were unable to believe their eyes.

"What sort o' wonder worker is this anyway?" they asked each other. "No human could ever throw the rope like that!"

Then Pecos Bill showed the men how it was done, and after two or three months of hard practice, each of them was able to make frequent catches at a distance of from ten to not more than twenty feet.

In the meantime, Pecos Bill had become dissatisfied with the fact that he couldn't find a longer rope. So he began to braid himself a cowhide lariat. This is how he went to work. First he looked up some old horned steers that had lived so many years within the depths of the trees that there were green algae on their backs—moss-backs, sure enough. What's more, these steers were so old their faces were gray and wrinkled.

Whenever Pecos Bill got hold of one of these old fellows, he first loosened the hide behind the ears. He then grasped the steer by the tail and with a flip of his wrists and forearm and a wild yowl, he frightened the animal so that it jumped out of its skin. The tough hides of these old moss-backs were just what Pecos needed.

Three or four years later when he had it finished, his loyal ranchers declared on all sides that the lariat was as long as the equator, and that Pecos could lasso anything this side of China.

It was thus that Pecos Bill solved one of the problems that had worried cowhands and their bosses for years.

The Parrot Who Wouldn't Say "Cataño"

a Puerto Rican folk tale by Pura Belpré

Across the bay from San Juan in Puerto Rico is a town called Cataño. Here, long ago, lived a retired sailor called Yuba. His only possession and sole companion was a parrot—a beautiful, talkative bird known to all the town. Much as the parrot talked, there was one thing she refused to say. That was the name of the town. No matter how hard Yuba tried to teach her, she would never say the word. This saddened Yuba who loved his town very much.

"You are an ungrateful bird," Yuba told the parrot. "You repeat everything you hear, yet refuse to say the name of the town where you have lived most of your life." But all the parrot would do was to blink her beady eyes and talk of other things.

One day as Yuba sat on his balcony with the parrot on his knee, arguing as usual, who should come by but Don Casimiro, the rich poultry fancier from San Juan. He stopped and listened. In all his years he had never heard such a parrot. What a wonderful addition to his poultry yard she would make! The more he listened to her conversation, the more he wanted to own her.

"Would you sell me that parrot?" he said at last. "I will pay you well for her."

"Neither silver nor gold can buy her, Señor," said Yuba.

63

Don Casimiro was surprised. To all appearances this man looked as if he could use some money. "What else would you take for her, my good man?" he asked.

"Nothing. But I will make a bargain with you," replied Yuba.

"A bargain? What kind of a bargain?" Don Casimiro wanted to know.

"I have been trying to teach her to say 'Cataño.' But for reasons of her own she refuses to say it. Well, take her with you. If you can make her say it, the bird is yours and I will be grateful to you for the rest of my life. If you fail, bring her back to me."

"Agreed," said Don Casimiro delightedly. He took the parrot, thanked Yuba and left.

Late that afternoon he returned home. He sat in the spacious corridor facing the courtyard filled with fancy fowls and potted plants. "Now," he said to the parrot, "repeat after me: *Ca-ta-ño!*" And he took great care to say each syllable clearly and slowly. The parrot flapped her wings, but said not a word.

"Come, come," said Don Casimiro. "Say *Ca-ta-ño.*" The parrot blinked her beady eyes at him, but said not a word.

"But you can say anything you want. I have heard you speak. Let's try it again. *Ca-ta-ño.*" Don Casimiro waited, but the parrot sauntered down the corridor as if she were deaf.

Now Don Casimiro was a man of great wealth but little patience. His temper was as hot as the chili peppers he grew in his vegetable patch. He strode after the parrot who had stopped beside a large potted fern at the end of the corridor. He grabbed the bird and shook her. "Say *CA-TA-ÑO!*" he commanded through clenched teeth.

The parrot blinked and quickly wriggled herself out of his hands. But Don Casimiro picked her up again and held her fast. "Say *Ca-ta-ño,* or I will wring your neck and throw you out of the window!"

The parrot said not a word.

Blinded with anger, Don Casimiro hurled her out of the window, forgetting to wring her neck. The parrot landed in the chicken coop.

That night a strange noise rose from the courtyard. Don Casimiro awoke with a start. "Thieves!" he cried.

Thinking they were after his fowls he rushed out of the house and headed for the chicken coop. What a turmoil! Chicken feathers flew every which way. Pails of water and chicken feed were overturned. Squawking chickens ran hither and thither; others lay flat on the ground as though they were dead.

Suddenly, from the far end of the coop rose a voice saying: "Say *Ca-ta-ño,* or I will wring your neck and throw you out of the window!"

There, perched on a rafter, was the parrot, clutching one of the most precious fowls. Don Casimiro rushed to the spot and pulled the parrot down.

Before the sun had risen he was aboard the ferry boat on the way to Yuba's home. The parrot sat on his knees as if she had forgotten the happenings of the night before. He found Yuba sitting on his balcony sipping a cup of black coffee.

"So you failed too," said Yuba sadly.

"Oh, no, no!" Don Casimiro replied. "She said 'Cataño' all right! But the bargain is off. I want you to take her back."

Yuba was puzzled.

Don Casimiro noticed his confusion and quickly added: "You see, she played havoc in my chicken house before she said 'Cataño.' "

Yuba's face shone with happiness. He took the parrot and held her close. He watched Don Casimiro hurrying down the street toward the ferry boat station.

"Say *Ca-ta-ño,*" he whispered to the parrot.

"Cataño, Cataño," the parrot replied.

And since that day no one was happier, in all of Cataño, than Yuba the retired sailor.

Casey at the Bat

a poem by Ernest Lawrence Thayer

It looked extremely rocky for the Mudville nine that day;
The score stood two to four, with but one inning left to play.
So, when Cooney died at second, and Burrows did the same,
A pallor wreathed the features of the patrons of the game.

A straggling few got up to go, leaving there the rest,
With that hope which springs eternal within the human breast.
For they thought: "If only Casey could get a whack at that,"
They'd put even money now, with Casey at the bat.

But Flynn preceded Casey, and likewise so did Blake,
And the former was a pudd'n, and the latter was a fake.
So on that stricken multitude a deathlike silence sat;
For there seemed but little chance of Casey's getting to the bat.

But Flynn let drive a "single," to the wonderment of all.
And the much-despiséd Blakey "tore the cover off the ball."
And when the dust had lifted, and they saw what had occurred,
There was Blakey safe at second, and Flynn a-huggin' third.

Then from the gladdened multitude went up a joyous yell—
It rumbled in the mountaintops, it rattled in the dell;
It struck upon the hillside and rebounded on the flat;
For Casey, mighty Casey, was advancing to the bat.

There was ease in Casey's manner as he stepped into his place;
There was pride in Casey's bearing and a smile on Casey's face;
And when responding to the cheers he lightly doffed his hat,
No stranger in the crowd could doubt 'twas Casey at the bat.

Ten thousand eyes were on him as he rubbed his hands with dirt,
Five thousand tongues applauded when he wiped them on his shirt;
Then when the writhing pitcher ground the ball into his hip,
Defiance glanced in Casey's eye, a sneer curled Casey's lip.

And now the leather-covered sphere came hurtling through the air,
And Casey stood a-watching it in haughty grandeur there.
Close by the sturdy batsman the ball unheeded sped;
"That ain't my style," said Casey. "Strike one," the umpire said.

From the benches black with people, there went up a muffled roar,
Like the beating of the storm waves on the stern and distant shore.
"Kill him! kill the umpire!" shouted someone on the stand;
And it's likely they'd have killed him had not Casey raised his hand.

With a smile of Christian charity great Casey's visage shone;
He stilled the rising tumult, he made the game go on;
He signaled to the pitcher, and once more the spheroid flew;
But Casey still ignored it, and the umpire said, "Strike two."

"Fraud!" cried the maddened thousands, and the echo answered
   "Fraud!"
But one scornful look from Casey, and the audience was awed;
They saw his face go stern and cold, they saw his muscles strain,
And they knew that Casey wouldn't let the ball go by again.

The sneer is gone from Casey's lips, his teeth are clenched in hate,
He pounds with cruel vengeance his bat upon the plate;
And now the pitcher holds the ball, and now he lets it go,
And now the air is shattered by the force of Casey's blow.

Oh, somewhere in this favored land the sun is shining bright,
The band is playing somewhere, and somewhere hearts are light;
And somewhere men are laughing, and somewhere children shout
But there is no joy in Mudville—Mighty Casey has struck out.

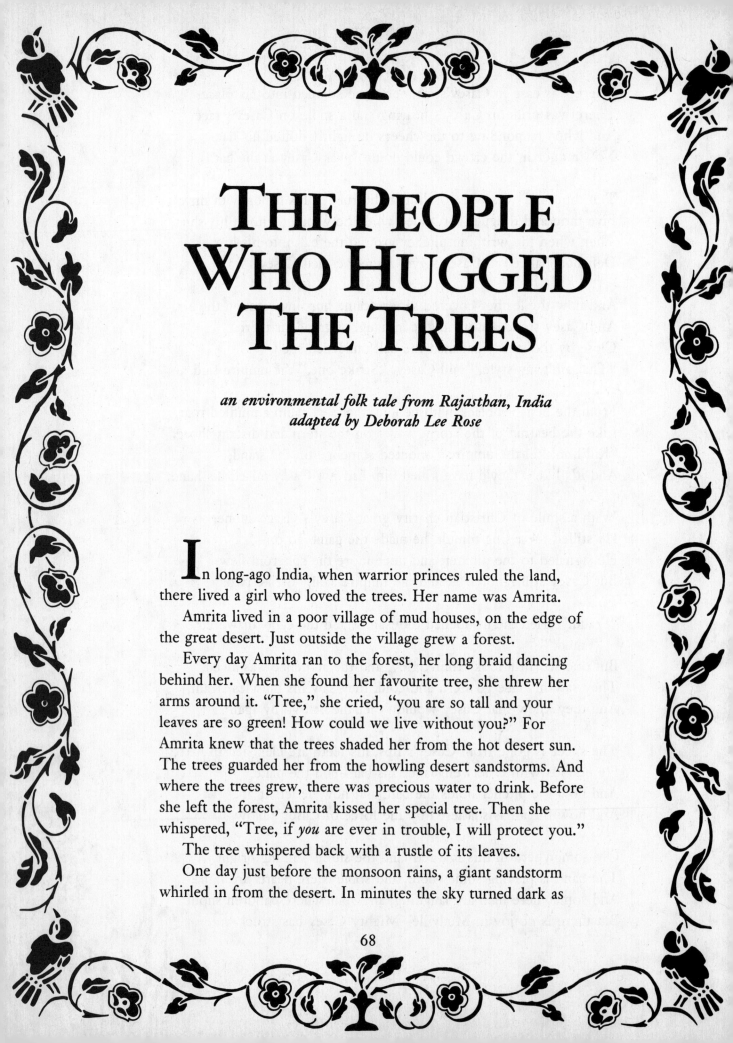

THE PEOPLE WHO HUGGED THE TREES

an environmental folk tale from Rajasthan, India
adapted by Deborah Lee Rose

In long-ago India, when warrior princes ruled the land,
there lived a girl who loved the trees. Her name was Amrita.

Amrita lived in a poor village of mud houses, on the edge of
the great desert. Just outside the village grew a forest.

Every day Amrita ran to the forest, her long braid dancing
behind her. When she found her favourite tree, she threw her
arms around it. "Tree," she cried, "you are so tall and your
leaves are so green! How could we live without you?" For
Amrita knew that the trees shaded her from the hot desert sun.
The trees guarded her from the howling desert sandstorms. And
where the trees grew, there was precious water to drink. Before
she left the forest, Amrita kissed her special tree. Then she
whispered, "Tree, if *you* are ever in trouble, I will protect you."

The tree whispered back with a rustle of its leaves.

One day just before the monsoon rains, a giant sandstorm
whirled in from the desert. In minutes the sky turned dark as

night. Lightning cracked the sky and wind whipped the trees as Amrita dashed for her house. From inside, she could hear the sand battering against the shutters. After the storm ended, there was sand everywhere—in Amrita's clothes, in her hair and even in her food.

But she was safe and so was her village, because the trees had stood guard against the worst of the storm.

As Amrita grew, so did her love for the trees. Soon she had her own children, and she took them to the forest with her.

"These are your brothers and sisters," she told them. "They shade us from the hot desert sun. They guard us from the terrible desert sandstorms. They show us where to find water to drink," she explained. Then Amrita taught her children to hug the trees as she did.

Each day when she left the forest, Amrita fetched water from the village well. She carried the water in a large clay pot, balanced on top of her head.

One morning by the well, Amrita spotted a troop of men armed with heavy axes. They were headed toward the forest. "Cut down every tree you can find," she heard the chief axeman say. "The Maharajah needs plenty of wood to build his new fortress."

The Maharajah was a powerful prince who ruled over many villages. His word was law. Amrita was afraid. "The tree-cutters will destroy our forest," she thought. "Then we will have no shade from the sun or protection from the sandstorms. We will have no way to find water in the desert!" Amrita ran to the forest and hid. From her hiding place, she could hear the *whack* of the axes cutting into her beloved trees.

Suddenly Amrita saw the chief axeman swing his blade toward her special tree.

"Do not cut down these trees!" she cried and jumped in front of her tree. "Stand back!" thundered the axeman. "Please, leave my tree," Amrita begged. "Chop me instead." She hugged the tree with all her strength. The axeman shoved her away and swung his blade. He could see only the tree he had been ordered

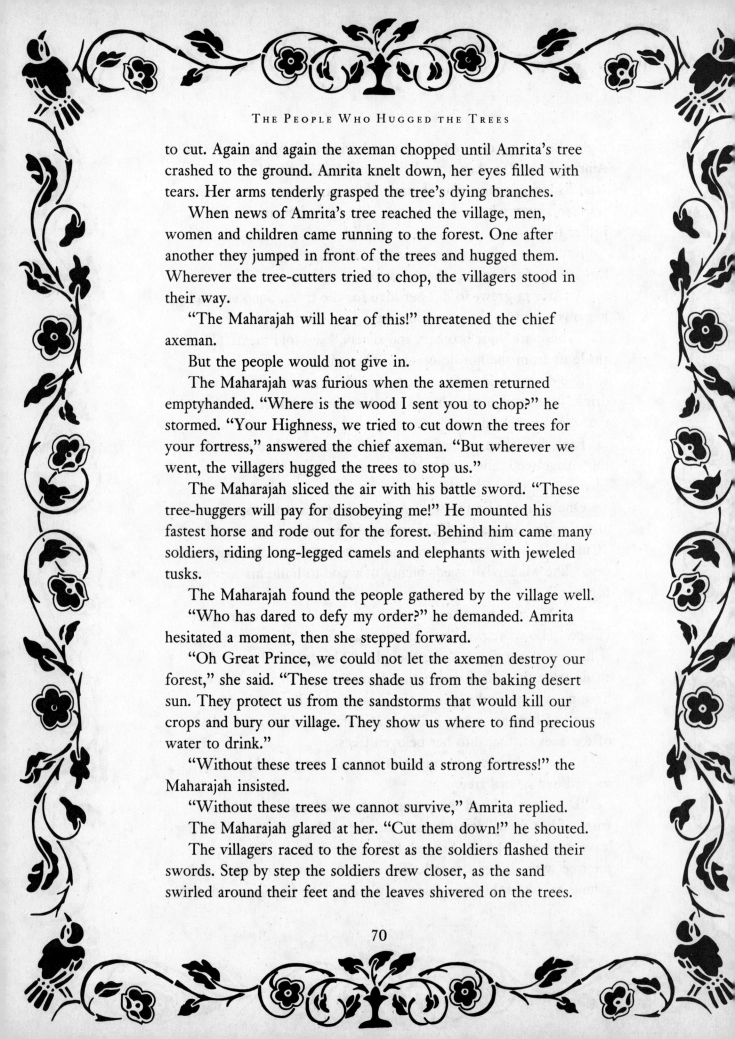

to cut. Again and again the axeman chopped until Amrita's tree crashed to the ground. Amrita knelt down, her eyes filled with tears. Her arms tenderly grasped the tree's dying branches.

When news of Amrita's tree reached the village, men, women and children came running to the forest. One after another they jumped in front of the trees and hugged them. Wherever the tree-cutters tried to chop, the villagers stood in their way.

"The Maharajah will hear of this!" threatened the chief axeman.

But the people would not give in.

The Maharajah was furious when the axemen returned emptyhanded. "Where is the wood I sent you to chop?" he stormed. "Your Highness, we tried to cut down the trees for your fortress," answered the chief axeman. "But wherever we went, the villagers hugged the trees to stop us."

The Maharajah sliced the air with his battle sword. "These tree-huggers will pay for disobeying me!" He mounted his fastest horse and rode out for the forest. Behind him came many soldiers, riding long-legged camels and elephants with jeweled tusks.

The Maharajah found the people gathered by the village well.

"Who has dared to defy my order?" he demanded. Amrita hesitated a moment, then she stepped forward.

"Oh Great Prince, we could not let the axemen destroy our forest," she said. "These trees shade us from the baking desert sun. They protect us from the sandstorms that would kill our crops and bury our village. They show us where to find precious water to drink."

"Without these trees I cannot build a strong fortress!" the Maharajah insisted.

"Without these trees we cannot survive," Amrita replied.

The Maharajah glared at her. "Cut them down!" he shouted.

The villagers raced to the forest as the soldiers flashed their swords. Step by step the soldiers drew closer, as the sand swirled around their feet and the leaves shivered on the trees.

Just when the soldiers reached the trees the wind roared in from the desert, driving the sand so hard they could barely see.

The soldiers ran from the storm, shielding themselves behind the trees. Amrita clutched her special tree and the villagers hid their faces as thunder shook the forest. The storm was worse than any the people had ever known. Finally, when the wind was silent, they came slowly out of the forest.

Amrita brushed the sand from her clothes and looked around. Broken tree limbs were scattered everywhere. Grain from the crops in the field littered the ground.

Around the village well drifts of sand were piled high, and Amrita saw that only the trees had stopped the desert from destroying the well and the rest of the village.

Just beyond the well the Maharajah stood and stared at the forest. He thought for a long time, then he spoke to the villagers.

"You have shown great courage and wisdom to protect your trees. From this day on your trees will not be cut," the Maharajah declared.

"Your forest will always remain a green place in the desert."

The people rejoiced when they heard the Maharajah's words. They sang and danced long into the night and lit up the sky with fireworks.

In the forest, the children strung flowers and bright colored paper through the branches of the trees. And where Amrita's tree had fallen, they marked a special place so they would never forget the tree's great sacrifice.

Many years have passed since that day, but some people say Amrita still comes to the forest to hug the trees.

"Trees," she whispers, "you are so tall and your leaves are so green! How could we live without you?"

For Amrita knows that the trees shade the people from the hot desert sun.

The trees guard the people from the howling desert sandstorms.

And where the trees grow there is water, and it is a good place for the people to live.

NOTE

In the original legend, Amrita Devi and several hundred villagers gave up their lives while protecting their forest, nearly three centuries ago. The Indian government has commemorated their sacrifice by naming the Rajasthani village of Khejare as India's first National Environment Memorial.

Today, the people of India still struggle to protect their environment. One of the most dedicated groups is the Chipko ("Hug the Tree") Movement, whose members support nonviolent resistance to the cutting of trees.

In 1987, the Chipko Movement received the distinguished Right Livelihood Award (the "alternative Nobel"), for "dedication to the conservation, restoration, and ecologically responsible use of India's natural resources."

HOW THE WHALE GOT HIS THROAT

a story by Rudyard Kipling

In the sea, once upon a time, O my Best Beloved, there was a Whale, and he ate fishes. He ate the starfish and the garfish, and the crab and the dab, and the plaice and the dace, and the skate and his mate, and the mackereel and the pickereel, and the really truly twirly-whirly eel. All the fishes he could find in all the sea he ate with his mouth—so! Till at last there was only one small fish left in all the sea, and he was a small 'Stute Fish, and he swam a little behind the Whale's right ear, so as to be out of harm's way. Then the Whale stood up on his tail and said, 'I'm hungry.' And the small 'Stute Fish said in a small 'stute voice, 'Noble and generous Cetacean, have you ever tasted Man?'

'No,' said the Whale. 'What is it like?'

'Nice,' said the small 'Stute Fish. 'Nice but nubbly.'

'Then fetch me some,' said the Whale, and he made the sea froth up with his tail.

'One at a time is enough,' said the 'Stute Fish. 'If you swim to latitude Fifty North, longitude Forty West (that is Magic), you will find, sitting *on* a raft, *in* the middle of the sea, with

nothing on but a pair of blue canvas breeches, a pair of suspenders (you must *not* forget the suspenders, Best Beloved), and a jack-knife, one shipwrecked Mariner, who, it is only fair to tell you, is a man of infinite-resource-and-sagacity.'

So the Whale swam and swam to latitude Fifty North, longitude Forty West, as fast as he could swim, and *on* a raft, *in* the middle of the sea, *with* nothing to wear except a pair of blue canvas breeches, a pair of suspenders (you must particularly remember the suspenders, Best Beloved), *and* a jack-knife, he found one single, solitary shipwrecked Mariner, trailing his toes in the water. (He had his Mummy's leave to paddle, or else he would never have done it, because he was a man of infinite-resource-and-sagacity.)

Then the Whale opened his mouth back and back and back till it nearly touched his tail, and he swallowed the shipwrecked Mariner, and the raft he was sitting on, and his blue canvas breeches, and the suspenders (which you *must* not forget), *and* the jack-knife—He swallowed them all down into his warm, dark, inside cupboards, and then he smacked his lips—so, and turned round three times on his tail.

But as soon as the Mariner, who was a man of infinite-resource-and-sagacity, found himself truly inside the Whale's warm, dark, inside cupboards, he stumped and he jumped and he thumped and he bumped, and he pranced and he danced, and he banged and he clanged, and he hit and he bit, and he leaped and he creeped, and he prowled and he howled, and he hopped and he dropped, and he cried and he sighed, and he crawled and he bawled, and he stepped and he lepped, and he danced hornpipes where he shouldn't, and the Whale felt most unhappy indeed. (*Have* you forgotten the suspenders?)

So he said to the 'Stute Fish, 'This man is very nubbly, and besides he is making me hiccough. What shall I do?'

'Tell him to come out,' said the 'Stute Fish.

So the Whale called down his own throat to the shipwrecked Mariner, 'Come out and behave yourself. I've got the hiccoughs.'

'Nay, nay!' said the Mariner. 'Not so, but far otherwise. Take me to my natal-shore and the white-cliffs-of-Albion, and I'll think about it.' And he began to dance more than ever.

'You had better take him home,' said the 'Stute Fish to the Whale. 'I ought to have warned you that he is a man of infinite-resource-and-sagacity.'

So the Whale swam and swam and swam, with both flippers and his tail, as hard as he could for the hiccoughs; and at last he saw the Mariner's natal-shore and the white-cliffs-of-Albion, and he rushed half-way up the beach, and opened his mouth wide and wide and wide, and said, 'Change here for Winchester, Ashuelot, Nashua, Keene, and stations on the *Fitch*burg Road'; and just as he said 'Fitch' the Mariner walked out of his mouth. But while the Whale had been swimming, the Mariner, who was indeed a person of infinite-resource-and-sagacity, had taken his jack-knife and cut up the raft into a little square grating all running criss-cross, and he had tied it firm with his suspenders (*now* you know why you were not to forget the suspenders!), and he dragged that grating good and tight into the Whale's throat, and there it stuck! Then he recited the following *Sloka*, which, as you have not heard it, I will now proceed to relate—

By means of a grating
I have stopped your ating.

For the Mariner he was also an Hi-ber-ni-an. And he stepped out on the shingle, and went home to his Mother, who had given him leave to trail his toes in the water; and he married and lived happily ever afterward. So did the Whale. But from that day on, the grating in his throat, which he could neither cough up nor swallow down, prevented him eating anything except very, very small fish; and that is the reason why whales nowadays never eat men or boys or little girls.

The small 'Stute Fish went and hid himself in the mud under the Door-sills of the Equator. He was afraid that the Whale might be angry with him.

The Sailor took the jack-knife home. He was wearing the blue canvas breeches when he walked out on the shingle. The suspenders were left behind, you see, to tie the grating with; and that is the end of *that* tale.

The Haystack Cricket and How Things Are Different Up in the Moon Towns

a story by Carl Sandburg

here is an old man with wrinkles like wrinkled leather on his face living among the cornfields on the rolling prairie near the Shampoo River.

His name is John Jack Johannes Hummadummaduffer. His cronies and the people who know him call him Feed Box.

His daughter is a cornfield girl with hair shining the way cornsilk shines when the corn is ripe in the fall time. The tassels of cornsilk hang down and blow in the wind with a rusty dark gold, and they seem to get mixed with her hair. Her name is Eva Evelyn Evangeline Hummadummaduffer. And her chums and the people who know her call her Sky Blue.

The eleventh month, November, comes every year to the corn belt on that rolling prairie. The wagons bring the corn from the fields in the harvest days and the cracks in the corncribs shine with the yellow and gold of the corn.

The harvest moon comes, too. They say it stacks sheaves of the November gold moonshine into gold cornshocks on the sky. So they say.

On those mornings in November that time of the year, the old man they call Feed Box sits where the sun shines against the boards of a corncrib.

The girl they call Sky Blue, even though her name is Eva Evelyn Evangeline Hummadummaduffer, she comes along one November morning. Her father is sitting in the sun with his back against a corncrib. And he tells her he always sits there every year listening to the mice in the cornfields getting ready to move into the big farmhouse.

"When the frost comes and the corn is husked and put in the corncribs, the fields are cleaned and the cold nights come. Papa mouse and mama mouse tell the little ones it is time to sneak into the cellar and the garret and the attic of the farmhouse," said Feed Box to Sky Blue.

"I am listening," she said, "and I can hear the papa mouse and the mama mouse telling the little ones how they will find rags and paper and wool and splinters and shavings and hair, and they will make warm nests for the winter in the big farmhouse—if no kits, cats nor kittycats get them."

The old man, Feed Box, rubbed his back and his shoulders against the boards of the corncrib and washed his hands almost as if he might be washing them in the gold of the autumn sunshine. Then he told this happening:

This time of the year, when the mouse in the field whispers so I can hear him, I remember one November when I was a boy.

One night in November when the harvest moon was shining and stacking gold cornshocks in the sky, I got lost. Instead of going home I was going away from home. And the next day and the next night instead of going home I was going away from home.

That second night I came to a haystack where a yellow and gold cricket was singing. And he was singing the same songs the crickets sing in the haystacks back home where the Hummadummaduffers raise hay and corn, in the corn belt near the Shampoo River.

And he told me, this cricket did, he told me when he listened soft if everything was still in the grass and the sky, he could hear golden crickets singing in the cornshocks the harvest moon had stacked in the sky.

I went to sleep listening to the singing of the yellow and gold crickets in that haystack. It was early in the morning, long before daylight, I guess, the two of us went on a trip away from the haystack.

We took a trip. The yellow and gold cricket led the way. "It is the call of the harvest moon," he said to me in a singing whisper. "We are going up to the moon towns where the harvest moon stacks the cornshocks on the sky."

We came to a little valley in the sky. And the harvest moon had slipped three little towns into that valley, three little towns named Half Moon, Baby Moon, and Silver Moon.

In the town of Half Moon they *look* out of the doors and *come in* at the windows. So they have taken all the doorbells off the doors and put them on the windows. Whenever we rang a doorbell we went to a window.

In the town of Baby Moon they had windows on the chimneys so the smoke can look out of the window and see the weather before it comes out over the top of the chimney. And whenever the chimneys get tired of being stuck up on the top of the roof, the chimneys climb down and dance in the cellar. We saw five chimneys climb down and join hands and bump heads and dance a laughing chimney dance.

In the town of Silver Moon the cellars are not satisfied. They say to each other, "We are tired of being under, always under." So the cellars slip out from being under, always under. They slip out and climb up on top of the roof.

And that was all we saw up among the moon towns of Half Moon, Baby Moon, and Silver Moon. We had to get back to the haystack so as to get up in the morning after our night sleep.

"This time of the year I always remember that November," said the old man, Feed Box, to his daughter, Sky Blue.

And Sky Blue said, "I am going to sleep in a haystack sometime in November just to see if a yellow and gold cricket will come with a singing whisper and take me on a trip to where the doorbells are on the windows and the chimneys climb down and dance."

The old man murmured, "Don't forget the cellars tired of being under, always under."

GLUSCABI AND THE GAME ANIMALS

an Abenaki story from the Northeastern United States
by Joseph Bruchac

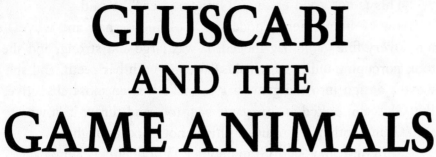

Long ago Gluscabi decided he would do some hunting. He took his bow and arrows and went into the woods.

But all the animals said to each other, "Ah-hah, here comes Gluscabi. He is hunting us. Let us hide from him."

So they hid and Gluscabi could not find them. He was not pleased. He went home to the little lodge near the big water where he lived with Grandmother Woodchuck.

"Grandmother," he said, "Make a game bag for me."

So Grandmother Woodchuck took caribou hair and made him a game bag. She wove it together tight and strong, and it was a fine game bag. But when she gave it to Gluscabi, he looked at it and then threw it down.

"This is not good enough," he said.

So then Grandmother Woodchuck took deer hair. She wove a larger and finer game bag and gave it to him. But Gluscabi looked at it and threw it down.

79

"This is not good enough, Grandmother," he said.

Now Grandmother Woodchuck took moose hair and wove him a very fine game bag indeed. It was large and strong, and she took porcupine quills which she flattened with her teeth, and she wove a design into the game bag to make it even more attractive. But Gluscabi looked at this game bag, too, and threw it down.

"Grandmother," he said, "This is not good enough."

"Eh, Gluscabi," said Grandmother Woodchuck, "how can I please you? What kind of game bag do you want?"

Then Gluscabi smiled, "Ah, Grandmother," he said, "make one out of woodchuck hair."

So Grandmother Woodchuck pulled all of the hair from her belly. To this day you will see that all woodchucks still have no hair there. Then she wove it into a game bag. Now this game bag was magical. No matter how much you put into it, there would still be room for more. And Gluscabi took this game bag and smiled.

"Oleohneh, Grandmother," he said. "I thank you."

Now Gluscabi went back into the woods and walked until he came to a large clearing. Then he called out as loudly as he could, "All you animals, listen to me. A terrible thing is going to happen. The sun is going to go out. The world is going to end and everything is going to be destroyed."

When the animals heard that, they became frightened. They came to the clearing where Gluscabi stood with his magic game bag.

"Gluscabi," they said, "What can we do? The world is going to be destroyed. How can we survive?"

Gluscabi smiled. "My friends," he said, "just climb into my game bag. Then you will be safe in there when the world is destroyed."

So all of the animals went into his game bag. The rabbits and the squirrels went in, and the game bag stretched to hold them. The raccoons and the foxes went in, and the game bag stretched larger still. The deer went in and the caribou went in. The bears went in and the moose went in, and the game bag stretched to hold them all. Soon all the animals in the world were in Gluscabi's game bag. Then Gluscabi tied the top of the game bag, laughed, slung it over his shoulder and went home.

"Grandmother," he said, "now we no longer have to go out and walk around looking for food. Whenever we want anything to eat we can just reach into my game bag."

Grandmother Woodchuck opened Gluscabi's game bag and looked inside. There were all of the animals in the world.

"Oh, Gluscabi," she said, "why must you always do things this way? You cannot keep all of the game animals in a bag. They will sicken and die. There will be none left for our children and our children's children. It is also right that it should be difficult to hunt them. Then you will grow stronger trying to find them. And the animals will also grow stronger and wiser trying to avoid being caught. Then things will be in the right balance."

"Kaamoji, Grandmother," said Gluscabi, "that is so." So he picked up his game bag and went back to the clearing. He opened it up. "All you animals," he called, "you can come out now. Everything is all right. The world was destroyed, but I put it back together again."

Then all of the animals came out of the magic game bag. They went back into the woods, and they are still there today because Gluscabi heard what his Grandmother Woodchuck had to say.

81

The Storytelling Stone

*a Seneca story
from the Northeastern
United States
by Joseph Bruchac*

Long ago, there were no stories in the world. Life was not easy for the people, especially during the long winters when the wind blew hard and the snow piled high about the longhouse.

One winter day a boy went hunting. He was a good hunter and managed to shoot several partridge. As he made his way back home through the snow, he grew tired and rested near a great rock which was shaped almost like the head of a person. No sooner had he sat down than he heard a deep voice speak.

"I shall now tell a story," said the voice.

The boy jumped up and looked around. No one was to be seen.

"Who are you?" said the boy.

"I am Great Stone," said the rumbling voice which seemed to come from within the Earth. Then the boy realized it was the big standing rock which spoke. "I shall now tell a story."

"Then tell it," said the boy.

"First you must give me something," said the stone. So the boy took one of the partridge and placed it on the rock.

"Now tell your story, Grandfather," said the boy.

Then the great stone began to speak. It told a wonderful story of how the Earth was created. As the boy listened he did not feel the cold wind and the snow seemed to go away. When the stone had finished the boy stood up.

"Thank you, Grandfather," said the boy. "I shall go now and share this story with my family. I will come back tomorrow."

The boy hurried home to the longhouse. When he got there he told everyone something wonderful had happened. Everyone gathered around the fire and he told them the story he heard from the great stone. The story seemed to drive away the cold and the people were happy as they listened and they slept peacefully that night, dreaming good dreams. The next day, the boy went back again to the stone and gave it another bird which he had shot.

"I shall now tell a story," said the big stone and the boy listened.

It went on this way for a long time. Throughout the winter the boy came each day with a present of game. Then Great Stone told him a story of the old times. The boy heard the stories of talking animals and monsters, tales of what things were like when the Earth was new. They were good stories and they taught important lessons. The boy remembered each tale and retold it to the people who gathered at night around the fire to listen. One day, though, when the winter was ending and the spring about to come, the great stone did not speak when the boy placed his gift of wild game.

"Grandfather," said the boy, "Tell me a story."

Then the great stone spoke for the last time. "I have told you all of my stories," said Great Stone. "Now the stories are yours to keep for the people. You will pass these stories on to your children and other stories will be added to them as years pass. Where there are stories, there will be more stories. I have spoken. Naho."

Thus it was that stories came into this world. To this day, they are told by the people of the longhouse during the winter season to warm the people. Whenever a storyteller finishes a tale, the people always give thanks, just as the boy thanked the storytelling stone long ago.

The
THEFT
of FIRE

a Maidu story from North America
retold by Stith Thompson

At one time the people had found fire, and were going to use it; but Thunder wanted to take it away from them, as he desired to be the only one who should have fire. He thought that if he could do this, he would be able to kill all the people. After a time he succeeded, and carried the fire home with him, far to the south. He put Woswosim (a small bird) to guard the fire, and see that no one should steal it. Thunder thought that people would die after he had stolen their fire, for they would not be able to cook their food; but the people managed to get along. They ate most of their food raw, and sometimes got Toyeskom (another small bird) to look for a long time at a piece of meat; and as he had a red eye, this after a long time would cook the meat almost as well as a fire. Only the chiefs had their food cooked in this way. All the people lived together in a big sweat-house. The house was as big as a mountain.

Among the people was Lizard and his brother; and they were always the first in the morning to go outside and sun themselves on the roof of the sweat-house. One morning as they lay there sunning themselves, they looked west, toward the Coast Range, and saw smoke. They called to all the other people, saying that they had seen smoke far away to the west. The people, however, would not believe them, and Coyote came out, and threw a lot of dirt and dust over the two. One of the people did not like this. He said to Coyote, "Why do you trouble people? Why don't you let others alone? Why don't you behave? You are always the first to start a quarrel. You always want to kill people without any reason." Then the other people felt sorry. They asked the two Lizards about what they had seen, and asked them to point out the smoke. The Lizards did so, and all could see the thin column rising up far to the west. One person said, "How shall we get that fire back? How shall we get it away from Thunder? He is a bad man. I don't know whether we had better try to get it or not." Then the chief said, "The best one among you had better try to get it. Even if Thunder is a bad man, we must try to get the fire. When we get there, I don't know how we shall get in but the one who is the best, who thinks he can get in, let him try." Mouse, Deer, Dog, and Coyote were the ones who were to try, but all the other people went too. They took a flute with them, for they meant to put the fire in it.

They travelled a long time, and finally reached the place where the fire was. They were within a little distance of Thunder's house, when they all stopped to see what they would do. Woswosim, who was supposed to guard the fire in the house, began to sing, "I am the man who never sleeps. I am the man who never sleeps." Thunder had paid him for his work in beads, and he wore them about his neck and around his waist. He sat on the top of the sweat-house, by the smoke-hole.

After a while Mouse was sent up to try and see if he could get in. He crept up slowly till he got close to Woswosim, and then saw that his eyes were shut. He was asleep, in spite of the song that he sang. When Mouse saw that the watcher was

asleep, he crawled to the opening and went in. Thunder had several daughters, and they were lying there asleep. Mouse stole up quietly, and untied the waist-string of each one's apron, so that should the alarm be given, and they jump up, these aprons or skirts would fall off, and they would have to stop to fix them. This done, Mouse took the flute, filled it with fire, then crept out, and rejoined the other people who were waiting outside.

Some of the fire was taken out and put in the Dog's ear, the remainder in the flute being given to the swiftest runner to carry. Deer, however, took a little, which he carried on the hock of his leg, where to-day there is a reddish spot. For a while all went well, but when they were about half-way back, Thunder woke up, suspected that something was wrong, and asked, "What is the matter with my fire?" Then he jumped up with a roar of thunder, and his daughters were thus awakened, and also jumped up; but their aprons fell off as they did so, and they had to sit down again to put them on. After they were all ready, they went out with Thunder to give chase. They carried with them a heavy wind and a great rain and a hailstorm, so that they might put out any fire the people had. Thunder and his daughters hurried along, and soon caught up with the fugitives, and were about to catch them, when Skunk shot at Thunder and killed him. Then Skunk called out, "After this you must never try to follow and kill people. You must stay up in the sky, and be the thunder. That is what you will be." The daughters of Thunder did not follow any farther; so the people went on safely, and got home with their fire, and people have had it ever since.

Pushing Up the Sky

*a Skagit story from the Pacific Northwest
told by Skagit elder Vi Hilbert*

A long time ago, the Creator was traveling across the land. His face shone so brightly that no one could look at him. He traveled from East to West, creating everything as he went along. He carried a great variety of languages. As he created each group of people, he gave them a special language.

Finally he arrived at the Puget Sound area—*my* country. He stopped and looked around. "This is such beautiful, beautiful land," he said. "I need go no further. I can stop right here, because this is the most beautiful land in the world."

The Creator still had many languages left, so he tossed these languages in all directions. That is the reason why there are so many different languages among the Indians of the Puget Sound area. After the Creator had scattered the languages around, the different groups of Indians found that they could not understand one another.

The people had another problem as well. The Creator had left the sky too low. Tall people were bumping their heads against the sky, and some people were climbing into the Sky World. This was not appropriate. There was an appropriate time to go into the Sky World, not just whenever people felt like it.

The wise people of the different groups had a meeting. They decided that if all the people pushed together, they could push the sky up higher. But because the Creator had given all of the animals, birds, insects, and people different languages, it would be difficult to make them understand when to push. Finally, one of the wise men said that if they had a signal, they could all push at the same time. He suggested that the signal should be one word, "Ya-hoh!", which means "proceed" in all the languages. All the other wise men agreed. They set the date for pushing up the sky, and scattered the news among the different groups.

Everyone was busy making tall poles with which to push up the sky. On the day set for lifting the sky, all of the people braced their poles against the sky and got ready to push. The old man gave the command, "Ya-hoh!" All the people pushed together, and the sky went up a little bit.

Again the old man called, "Ya-HOH!" Everyone pushed again, and the sky went up a little further.

Yet again the old man yelled, "Ya-HOH!" Everyone pushed harder, and the sky rose even further.

A fourth time the old man shouted, *"Ya-HOH!"* The people pushed as hard as they could, and the sky rose to where it is today.

However, while most of the people were pushing up the sky, there were a few hunters chasing some elk. The hunters weren't paying any attention to what was going on around them. The elk jumped into the Sky World as the sky was being pushed up, and the hunters jumped right up after them. The elk and the hunters got stuck up in that Sky World, and they are still there today. They are the stars in the Big Dipper, way up there in the sky. The three hunters form the handle of the dipper. The one in the center is leading his dog, the tiny star so close to him. The four elk form the rest of the dipper.

There were also some fishermen that day who were so busy fishing that they were not paying any attention to what was going on around them. As the sky was being lifted, those fishermen got stuck up in the Sky World, too. They became the stars in the Skatefish up in the sky.

So because all the people worked together to push up the sky that day, we are told, "You can do a lot if you work together." And because of what happened to the hunters and the fishermen when they weren't paying attention, we are told, "Always be alert."

THE BOY WHO CAUGHT THE WIND

a story from the Thompson River people of Canada
by Edythe W. Newell

The wind in the Far North was a terrible thing. It was an enemy no one saw, and it came whirling and swirling, day or night, over the country.

Wind broke the trees and dropped them on the forest floor. It tore down the summer lodges and killed the people. When the people shouted in anger at Wind, it would not listen. Truly, Wind was a terrible thing.

A man and his son lived in a lodge in that village which was in the magic place where the hills fold into themselves, near the Place of the Winds. The young boy thought a lot about many things. He was always trying to do magic.

One day the son spoke to his father about Wind.

"Father," he said, "Wind is our enemy. It does much harm to our people. I will capture Wind."

His father laughed, saying, "How can you do that, and you are so small? You cannot see Wind. It has no form. Do not be foolish, my son. Wind cannot be captured."

But the boy would not be discouraged. Although he said no more to his father, he was determined to capture Wind. He studied his traps and chose a snare to catch Wind.

Alone, the young boy went out into the night to the Place of the Winds and set the trap. He hid himself behind a fallen tree and watched carefully. He soon saw that he had made his trap too large.

So each night, the boy returned alone in the dark of the night and made the snare a little smaller until one night—he caught Wind!

Now Wind did not know what had happened. It was surprised to find that something had stopped it. Never before could anything hold Wind, and no thing had stood where Wind wanted to go.

Wind was angry! It flattened itself and blew its hardest. But the boy held the trap, and it did not break. Wind stood in the snare and whirled itself into a tall tower. But the boy held the trap, and it did not break.

Wind struggled with the boy for a long time. At last the boy pushed Wind into his blanket and tied the corners carefully. That done, the young boy carried Wind home in the blanket.

The boy's father was amazed. And he was well pleased, too. This was an important thing that his son had done. The father held a feast to honor the young boy, and he called all the people to come to see this thing.

There was one difficulty. The people did not believe that Wind was caught in the blanket. They laughed at the boy.

"We will not believe such a story," they said. "Wind wrapped up in your blanket, you say? What a silly tale to tell!"

And they all laughed at the father and his son. What a joke!

The boy was not afraid of their laughter. He knew that he told the truth. His back became very straight as he stood before them. With much ceremony he opened one corner of the blanket and angry Wind rushed out so wildly that the lodge was nearly blown apart.

Then the people believed and were afraid. They tried to hide. They begged the boy to stop the blowing of the wind. But no one offered to help.

Wind struggled fiercely, but somehow the boy finally pushed it back into the blanket and tied the four corners firmly together.

Now Wind thought that it could not endure the humiliation of this second capture. It roared and it howled in the blanket, but the boy would not let it go. While Wind screamed in fury the boy would not listen.

At last Wind stopped howling and suggested that he and the boy make an agreement. The boy was willing to do this, but he wanted to be sure that the forests and the lodges of the people would be safe from the angry wind. He insisted that Wind must find a way to live without harming the people.

Wind considered that this was fair and gave a promise to the boy. Wind explained that sometimes it must blow very hard across the land but that it would send a warning to the people. To warn the people of its coming, Wind promised to make the sky red.

And so the boy let Wind go free.

Now, whirling and swirling, Wind blows from the four corners all through the land. And when the sky is red in the morning, the people get ready because they know Wind will be blowing hard.

Little Burnt Face

an Algonquin story
from the Northeast
woodlands
by Dorothy de Wit

IN THE DAYS OF OUR GRAND-
FATHERS THERE WAS A LARGE LAKE
surrounded by birch forests. On one side of
the lake there was a village in which lived a
man and his three daughters. The older girls
were capable and good-looking, but they were
concerned only with themselves. The
youngest was very pretty, but she was shy and
frail. Her mother had died when she was
born, and in his sorrow, the father often went
on long hunting trips, leaving the girl in the
care of the older sisters. And since they
wanted to be free to do as they chose, as the
years passed they left more and more of the
household chores for the youngest. Sometimes
the small girl stumbled under the heavy loads
of sticks for the fire; sometimes she was bent
almost double under the weight of heavy
water carriers. And she was often so tired
grinding corn and preparing the food for her
sisters that she sat alone by the fire, not even
wanting to eat. Then the sisters would laugh
at her, mock her ragged dress, and more than
once would push her so close to the fire that

92

the hot ashes flew up and burned her face and arms, and the hot coals scorched her feet. Sometimes the hot sparks flew into her hair and singed it so that it was scraggly and rough. The villagers looked at her singed hair and burned skin and they laughed and called her Little Burnt Face. When the father returned from his hunting and questioned the older girls, they would tell him that the little girl was careless and did not obey their warnings and often went too near the fire or hurt herself in other ways.

Little Burnt Face did not complain, but she was lonely and wished her father were at home more often. One time, when he returned from a hunting trip, he brought back a quantity of the white shells from which wampum was made. The girls set about stringing the pretty shells. Little Burnt Face also made strings of them, hoping that when she wore them, they would hide some of her scars.

At the far end of the lake there was a large lodge in which there lived a strange and mysterious person. His sister kept his wigwam for him, and when the red sun laid a path from the west across the lake to his doorway, the villagers could hear the lapping of the water against his returning canoe. They could see the game—deer, squirrel, rabbit, or fowl—that he dropped in front of the wigwam. They could see the moccasins his sister hung for him. But he himself was not to be seen. It was rumored that he was wonderful and strong, and they called him the Invisible One. Great was the curiosity of every maid in the village, for it was known that he sought a wife. However, he would accept only the one who could see him as he truly was. His sister let it be known that any girl in the village might come to the lakeside at sunset when her brother returned each day. But it would be the maid who could say what he used for his shoulder strap, and what his bowstring was made of, who would become his wife.

Every evening some of the girls would braid their hair with shells and beads, don their best robes, and go to the lakeshore. But as yet not one of them had known the answer or seen the Invisible One.

One day the two older sisters made themselves lovely and dressed their hair till it shone. At sunset they went to the great one's sister and waited for the splashing sound of his paddle. When they heard it, the Invisible One's sister asked, "Do you see my brother now? Do you truly see him?"

Both girls answered at once, "Yes. Indeed we see him," though they saw nothing at all.

"And of what is his bowstring made?" she asked.

93

One of the girls said, "It is a green withe of the ash tree."

And the other girl said, "It is made of rawhide."

Both materials were commonly used to make bowstrings. But the sister of the Invisible One shook her head and led them back to their own wigwam. "You did not truly see my brother," she said.

The sisters were cross and unhappy. They vented their temper on Little Burnt Face, pushing her into the hot coals till she cried with pain.

Nevertheless, on the following day Little Burnt Face rose early before the others wakened and bathed in the lake. She too wished to visit the lodge of the Invisible One. But though she was clean, her rags were so ugly! She went deep into the birch forest and pulled off large sheets of the white outer bark of the trees, saying as she did so, "My brother birch tree, give me some of your fair white skin that I may make a dress for myself and not be shamed! I will stitch flowers and birch leaves around its hem to make it beautiful!" And Little Burnt Face scraped on the thin birch bark figures of the forest creatures and flowering vines. Then she sewed the strips of bark together to make a loose gown, which she tied with a sash made of leaves and strong vine fibers woven together. She put flowers in her singed hair and a string of the wampum shells around her neck, but for her bare feet she had only a pair of her father's large old moccasins that had to be tied on lest they fall off her feet. She made her way to the lakeshore amid the laughter and scorn of the villagers. Her sisters mocked her: "Oh, indeed the Invisible One should see this! He'll paddle to the other side of the lake very quickly!" But Little Burnt Face lifted her singed head and scarred face proudly and walked on in the direction of the great wigwam as the sun was setting.

The sister of the Invisible One saw her coming; she heard, too, the laughter of the others, and she went out to greet Little Burnt Face. "You too wish to meet my brother? Come, let us wait here at the water's edge. We shall soon hear the sound of his paddle."

Little Burnt Face waited with her, half afraid and shy, but eager to see if she might catch a glimpse of the great one. In time, there came the sound of water lapping against a canoe and the drip of water falling from a paddle. "Now, Little Burnt Face! Look into the sun! Do you see my brother?"

Burnt Face leaned forward, and her eyes searched the water; then a strange glow spread across her face! It was a glow of amazement, of wonder. "Yes—ah, yes! I do see him! How great he is—how beautiful!"

The sister asked, "If you see him, tell me of what his bowstring is made?"

For a moment Little Burnt Face was still; then she said, "It is— yes, I am sure it is—the rainbow!"

Surprise flickered over the sister's face, and she asked again, "And his shoulder strap with which he pulls his game—of what is that made?"

Little Burnt Face shook her head. "It cannot be, yet I think truly it must be—the Milky Way itself! Ahhhh—what a great, great wonder!"

Then the sister smiled with joy and turned Little Burnt Face toward the lodge. "My child, it is indeed as you say. My brother, the Invisible One, will come shortly to our lodge, and we must be ready for him. Come, let us prepare ourselves." So saying, she brought Little Burnt Face to the lodge. She prepared warm water scented with herbs and pine resin, and as she bathed the girl, all the ugly scars disappeared. Then she washed the scraggly stiff hair and combed it softly with a comb from her own chest, and as she combed the hair, it grew longer and longer and shone like the wing of a blackbird! From her chest, she brought out a gown of softest white deerskin, finely beaded, and on Little Burnt Face's feet she placed small moccasins embroidered and quilled. Little Burnt Face shone with a beauty no one had seen before!

The sound of footsteps approaching brought the sister to the opening of the wigwam. She pulled Little Burnt Face forward to meet the Invisible One, for suddenly the girl felt shy and lowered her eyes.

"So we have found each other at last!" The voice was deep and quiet.

Then Little Burnt Face felt such a rush of joy she put out her hands and laughed! "Yes!" she said. "Yes, we have found each other!" She moved to his side and sat beside him in the wife's place as the darkness fell across the water.

THE JAZZY THREE BEARS

a rap version of the traditional tale

This version of "The Jazzy Three Bears" was transcribed from memory by Jocelyn (age 9) and Dawn (age 7) Lippert, who learned it from Mary Cay Brass at Pinewoods Camp in Massachusetts during the summer of 1991. Brass learned it 7 years before from a group of children at a school where she was teaching at the time. Other versions of "The Jazzy Three Bears" have been recorded by Cathy Fink, Connie Regan and Barbara Freeman, and Doug Eliot. Canada's jazz singer Jackie Washington recorded a version with a swinging piano backup in the 1940s.

This version, recorded by Dawn and Jocelyn and their friend Amber Bliven on the audiocassette which is offered with the Teacher's Read Aloud Anthology, was selected because children can recite it without instrumental accompaniment.

Once upon a time in a wee little cottage
There were three bears, chaaaa, chaaaa, cha.
One was a papa bear and one was a mama bear
And one was a wee bear, chaaaa, cha.

One day they went a-walking in the deep woods a-talking,
When along, along, along came a pretty girl
With blond hair and blue eyes, and her name was Goldilocks
And upon the door she knocked, but no one was there,
No, no one was there.

So she walked right in and had a ball.
She didn't care, no, she didn't care.
And when she got tired she went upstairs.
Home, home, home came the three bears,
Cha, cha.

"Someone's been eating my porridge,"
Said the papa bear, nah, nah, nah, nah, nah, nah, nah.
"Someone's been eating my porridge,"
said the mama bear, nah, nah, nah, nah, nah, nah, nah.
"Hey, Bobba-ree-bear," said the little wee bear
"SOME-ONE HAS BRO-KEN MY CHAIR. CRASH!"
Just then Goldilocks woke up, broke up
The story and beat it out of there.

"Good-bye, bye. Bye," said the papa bear.
"Good-bye, bye. Bye," said the mama bear.
"Hey, Bobba-ree-bear," said the little wee bear.

So ends the story of the three little bears.
Nah, nah, nah, nah, nah, nah, nah, nah, nah, nah, nah. Chaaaa!!

BEAUTY
AND THE
BEAST

a French fairy tale by Madame LePrince de Beaumont
adapted by Amy Ehrlich

A rich merchant in a far-off land had for many years been lucky in all his undertakings. His three daughters danced in jeweled ball gowns and his three sons rode Arabian steeds that moved like the wind.

Then one day for no reason the merchant suddenly lost everything. His house caught fire and burned to the ground, and all his ships at sea were sunk or plundered by pirates. Only a small country cottage remained to him, and the merchant was forced to move there with his children. The two older daughters grumbled continually, regretting the lost amusements of their past. But the youngest, who was called Beauty, tried her best to comfort her father and brothers.

After many months the merchant got news that one of his ships, which he believed was lost, had come safely into port. His children came to see him off on his journey to the harbor town, naming the presents he must buy them. But Beauty did not ask for anything. When her father pressed her, she said she only wished for his safe return. "But surely, Beauty, there is some small treasure I may bring you," he said.

"If you see a rose along the way, you might pick it for me," she answered. "It is my favorite flower and it does not grow near here."

98

Then the merchant set out and reached the town. He soon discovered that his companions, believing him dead, had divided all the goods between them. Thus he was forced to return home, poorer even than he had started.

The way led through a deep forest, and it was snowing so bitterly that his horse could hardly carry him farther. Just when the merchant was about to give up hope, he saw a track that opened into an avenue lined with orange trees. To his surprise no snow had fallen there and the air smelled sweet and warm.

Soon the merchant came to a courtyard and then he went inside a vast castle. He passed through many splendid rooms but no one answered when he called out. The place seemed entirely empty and a deep silence was everywhere. At last he saw a small sitting room where a cheerful fire was blazing. A table was set with all manner of wines and meats, and as the merchant was very hungry, he lost no time in beginning the meal. Afterward he looked again for his host to thank him but, finding no one, he lay down upon a couch before the fire and fell fast asleep.

When he awoke he was refreshed and ready to continue his journey. Just as he was passing out of the courtyard, he saw a hedge of roses. Remembering Beauty's request, he stopped and gathered one to bring to her. But no sooner had he done so than a hideous beast appeared. His face was so ugly that the man could not bear to look at it.

The beast spoke in a terrible voice. "So this, then, is how you show your gratitude? Was it not enough that I allowed you in my castle and was kind to you?"

The merchant fell to his knees. "Oh, please, noble beast, do not take my life. I only picked the rose for my daughter, Beauty, who begged me to get her one."

On hearing this, the beast said gruffly, "I will forgive you only if you send one of your daughters to die in your stead. She must come willingly or else I will not have her. Now you may stay and rest in my castle until tomorrow."

Although the merchant found an excellent supper laid for him, he could not eat; nor could he sleep, although everything had been provided for his comfort. The next morning he set out again on a fine horse that the beast had left him.

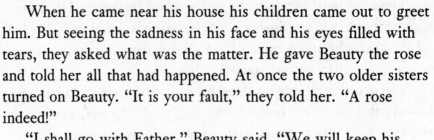

When he came near his house his children came out to greet him. But seeing the sadness in his face and his eyes filled with tears, they asked what was the matter. He gave Beauty the rose and told her all that had happened. At once the two older sisters turned on Beauty. "It is your fault," they told her. "A rose indeed!"

"I shall go with Father," Beauty said. "We will keep his promise to the beast."

Her father and her brothers, who loved her, begged Beauty to change her mind, but nothing would sway her. Go she must, and so they set out the very next morning, riding together on the beast's horse. When they reached the avenue of orange trees, the statues were holding flaming torches and fireworks flared in the sky. The palace gates opened of themselves and Beauty and her father walked into a room where a delicious meal awaited them.

Hardly had they finished eating when they heard the beast's footsteps echoing on the marble floor. Beauty clung to her father in terror, but the beast spoke to them in a mild tone and inquired about their journey. "Have you come here willingly, Beauty, to die in place of your father?" he said at last.

"Yes, willingly, and I know that I must stay," she said, looking at his face and trying to keep her voice from trembling.

"That is good," the beast answered. "Your father may spend the night but must go home in the morning." He bowed and took his leave of them.

Beauty tried to comfort her father when they parted by saying that the beast did not seem very cruel. Perhaps he would relent and one day allow her to return home.

She watched him ride off and then walked up a curving stairway into a room with mirrors all around. On the door was written in golden letters "Beauty's Room," and in the mornings a clock awakened her by calling her name softly twelve times. She was alone all day but when she was having her supper the beast would draw the curtains and come in. He spoke to her so pleasantly that she soon lost much of her fear of him.

Each night just before he left, he turned toward her and said, "Am I very ugly?"

100

"Yes," replied Beauty, "but you are so kind to me that I no longer mind."

"Will you marry me then?" he asked.

"Pray do not ask me," said Beauty.

"Since you will not, then good night, Beauty." And the beast would go away.

The castle was full of galleries and apartments containing rare and precious things. In one room was a cage filled with exotic birds. In another a troop of monkeys of all sizes came to meet her, making low bows. Beauty was enchanted with them and asked the beast if she might have one to keep her company. At once two young apes appeared and two small monkeys with them. They chattered and jumped all around her, making Beauty laugh.

Each night at suppertime the beast came to see her. Gradually she came to know him and liked him more and more. But to his question, "Beauty, will you marry me?" she always said, "No, Beast," very gently. And when she said these words, it seemed to her that he was sad and in some way disappointed with her.

Though Beauty had everything she could wish for and was content there, she never stopped missing her father and her brothers and sisters. At last one evening she begged the beast to let her go home.

"Ah, Beauty, will you desert an unhappy beast so easily? Very well, then. You shall visit your home but must promise to return in two months' time. You will not need any horse to carry you back. Only take this ring and turn it twice upon your finger the night before you come away and in the morning you will be with me."

The beast told her to take all that she wanted from the castle as presents for her family and he gave her two trunks. Though Beauty heaped them to the top with gold and trinkets, there always seemed to be more room, and they were not filled until she was tired of packing them. She went to sleep, but in the morning when she awoke she was in a strange place. Suddenly she heard her father's voice and knew that she was home.

Her sisters and brothers greeted her joyfully. But though their fortunes had changed and they were living in the town again, their entertainments seemed hollow and Beauty often thought of the castle, where she had been so happy. As the weeks went by she spoke of returning, but her father and brothers begged her to stay and she had not the courage to say goodbye to them.

The ring the beast had given her was on her dressing stand and one night Beauty put it on and gazed into the stone. Slowly an image appeared and she saw the beast in a far part of the castle gardens. He was lying on his back and seemed to be dying. In a panic Beauty grasped the ring and turned it around two times.

In the morning she was at the beast's castle. She searched everywhere but could not find him. At last she ran to the place in the gardens she had dreamed of and came upon the beast lying among the high bushes. Beauty put her head down on his chest but at first he was not breathing. Then she began to weep. "Oh, he is dead and it is on my account," she said, and her tears fell upon his face.

Slowly the beast opened his eyes.

"Oh, Beast, how you frightened me!" Beauty cried. "I never before knew how much I loved you."

"Can you really care for such an ugly creature as I am?" said the beast faintly.

"Yes, oh yes, dear Beast. Only live to be my husband and I will be your wife forever."

The moment Beauty uttered these words, a dazzling light shone everywhere. The palace windows glittered with lamps, and music was heard all around. To Beauty's great wonder a handsome prince stood before her. He said that her words had broken the spell of a magician, who had doomed him to wear the form of a beast. This terrible enchantment could be broken only when a maiden loved him in spite of his ugliness.

Then the grateful prince claimed Beauty as his bride. Her family was sent for and the wedding was celebrated the very next day.

The
MOUSE BRIDE

*a fairy tale from India
retold by Lucia Turnbull*

A farmer and his wife had no children ... but one year, in the season of ploughing, a strange thing happened to them.

Each evening as he came to the end of his day's work, the Farmer would lean on his plough and lament aloud, "My neighbours all have sons who will plough their fields when they are old and feeble. But I have none. What will become of my land? Oh, if I only had a son! Oh, that a son would fall down from the sky!"

One evening—when he was saying this as usual—a hawk flew over his head, and wondering, I suppose, to hear an old man talking to himself, he spread his claws in surprise, and out there dropped a mouse ... a little mouse, a boy-mouse. And he fell at the feet of the Farmer.

The Farmer picked him up, saying, "Where have you come from?"

"Out of the sky," replied the Mouse simply.

"Will you come home with me?" asked the Farmer.

"Yes, sir if you like," agreed the Mouse.

"Will you learn to plough and sow and reap?" continued the Farmer.

"My goodness, I can do that already!" squeaked the Mouse, very much amused.

103

So the farmer carried him home and set him down on the
table. But when the Farmer's wife came in from the yard, she
gave a piercing shriek.

"Look, husband, look!" she cried, clutching her sari around
her. "Look, there's a mouse on the table!"

"That is our son," explained the Farmer gravely.

"A mouse! Our son!" exclaimed the wife.

For a moment she thought her husband had been out in the
sun too long, and was raving.

"This little fellow dropped out of the sky," said the Farmer.

But the Mouse was very frightened. "Why is she shrieking?"
he asked piteously.

"I do not know," replied the Farmer. "She was not
expecting you—yes, that is it, she's taken by surprise. Enough!"
he said to his wife, and gave her a shake to steady her.

But now she was really looking at the Mouse, and suddenly
she smiled.

"Why, husband, you are right," she said; "yes, yes, it is
our son."

And she hugged the boy-mouse and gave him food, then put
him to bed. And in the morning she made him a little red coat,
and he strode off into the fields with his newly-found father.

It was quite true what he had said, that he could plough and
sow and reap. Very well he did it—some days better than the
Farmer himself. Nothing could tire him. All day long he worked,
ploughing late into the evening, his paws clenched on the
handles of the plough, his face set in a frown, and his whiskers
gleaming red with the setting sun.

Then the Farmer would call to him, "Come on, my dear,
come home. Look how late it is."

The Mouse looked up at the sky, then answered steadily, "I
can still see to plough, Father."

"But, look, all my neighbours' sons have gone home to
supper," said the Farmer.

"Have they all gone?" The Mouse looked round as he spoke.
"Are the fields quite empty?"

"There's Rama in the next field, just packing up," was the reply.

"I shall plough until he has gone." And the Mouse gripped the handles of the plough, to show that he meant what he said.

"Don't tire yourself, my son." The Farmer spoke kindly, for he had grown to love his adopted son very deeply.

"I am a strong mouse," said the little creature.

Not until the fields were empty would he stop work, and when he got home he would be merry and sing to please his parents.

The Farmer was so proud of him; he thought there was no better son on earth. But after a time the little animal was no longer merry, he sang no more; and though he ploughed as well and as long as ever, he was a different mouse when he came home at night.

Then the Farmer was grieved, but his wife—who knew other things than ploughing—took a measure, and when the mouse was asleep, measured the length of his tail.

"Why are you doing that?" asked the Farmer.

"Hush!" replied the wife; "hush, and I will tell you. Seven inches—exactly. What's three times seven, husband?"

The Farmer thought for a moment. "Three sevens? Hmph! . . . three sevens are twenty-one."

The Farmer's wife gave a delighted nod.

"Yes, yes, I thought so!" she whispered.

"What did you think?" the Farmer whispered back.

"Our little boy-mouse has become a man," she replied softly.

"A man!" echoed the Farmer. "But why is he sad?"

His wife put the measure away.

"He is sad, husband, because he needs a wife," she said, and she looked tenderly at the sleeping mouse, who gave a tiny sigh as he snuggled in more cosily.

"If it's a wife he wants, I'll go and find him one," said the Farmer stoutly.

"Yes, tomorrow," agreed the woman. "But mind you, husband, she must be the best wife in the world to be worthy of our wonderful son."

The Farmer moved off towards the fire. "She must be like him, neither better nor worse," he grunted.

And so the very next day, the little man-mouse in his red coat, and the Farmer, his adopted father, set out to look for a wife. And all day long they searched and found no one. As the sun set, they sat down on a stone; the Farmer was quite worn out, and even the Mouse was beginning to yawn.

Suddenly, the Moon stepped up into the sky, dazzling the Farmer with her beauty.

"Look, look, my son!" he cried. "There is a wife worthy of you. What do you think of her?"

The Mouse looked up at the Moon until he blinked. She was bright, she was radiant, but he did not much care for her.

So he turned to the Farmer, and said, "True, she is very beautiful, Father, but she is so cold and proud."

"Yes, I am cold," scoffed the Moon; "I am proud. I am not for you."

The Farmer got up and made a deep salaam. "Tell me, my lady Moon, is there none better than you?"

"Oh yes," replied the Moon. "There is the cloud. When she covers me with her mantle I am invisible. She is better than I."

At that moment a cloud slipped over the Moon, and hid her from sight.

"Look, look, my son!" said the Farmer. "There is a wife worthy of you. What do you think of her?"

"She is very fine," agreed the Mouse. "But she's sad and gloomy."

"Tell me, Lady Cloud," said the Farmer, "is there none better than you?"

"Oh, yes!" replied the Cloud, "there is the Wind. She drives me all round the sky. She is better than I."

And at once the Wind blew hard, and scattered the Cloud.

And now the Farmer thought he had found a fine wife for the Mouse, and said, "The Wind now! She's just the one for you." What do you think of her?"

The Mouse shivered. "She sets my whiskers a-flutter, father, but she fidgets so," he complained.

"Yes, I am restless," whistled the Wind. "I am not for you."

"Tell me, Lady Wind," said the Farmer, "is there none better than you?"

"The Mountain," replied the Wind promptly. "She is far better than I, for although I storm, I cannot move her."

And the Farmer and the Mouse turned round, and saw that they were sitting at the foot of a mighty mountain.

"There!" exclaimed the Farmer with relief. "At last we have found a wife worthy of you. Now then what do you think of her?"

"She is very noble, father, but I think she would be obstinate," replied the Mouse.

"Yes, I am obstinate," boomed the Mountain. "I am not for you."

"Alas, alas!" lamented the Farmer. "Alas, my son! It seems as if we shall never find you a wife! Tell me, Lady Mountain, is there none better than you?"

Then the Mountain groaned, and said, "There is one far better, for though I am obstinate and do not budge, I know of one who will some day destroy me. Dig, dig into my heart. Dig deep!"

Then the Farmer took a spade, and the Mouse dug with his paws, and they made a hole in the Mountain, and were digging when the Mountain groaned again.

"Listen," she begged of them, "oh, listen! Do you not hear?"
And they listened.

"I hear nothing," said the Farmer.

"Set your ear to the ground," said the Mountain.

So they set their ears to the ground, and the Mouse's ear was the keener, it was so large and round.

"I hear a sound of scratching!" he cried in excitement.

The Farmer listened again.

"I hear it, too!" he shouted. "Yes, it is most certainly something scratching."

"It is what I told you," sighed the Mountain. "Dig on. It is in my heart."

So the Farmer dug, and the Mouse dug, and the noise from the other side grew louder ... scratch, scratch, SCRATCH! And suddenly, the earth broke away before them, and all they could see was a gaping hole, black and deep, reaching into the Mountain's heart.

Together they spoke in whispers into the hole, "Come out, come out! Come out, whoever you are!"

And there stepped forth from the darkness, a lady-mouse!

She wore a cloak of grey silk, her gloves were shell pink, and between her ears was a diadem of dewdrops. And the Farmer would have spoken—would have asked him how he liked her—but the man-mouse held up his paw.

"Do not speak," he said, as if under an enchantment. "This is the lady who must be my wife."

And he gave her his arm, and they walked home slowly together, the Farmer following, a light of wonder in his eyes.

When they reached home the Farmer put his finger to his lips, and his wife nodded.

For she, you remember, knew other things than ploughing.

MARGARET H. LIPPERT is a professional storyteller who comes from a family of Irish storytellers. A classroom teacher for many years, she taught children's literature and storytelling at Bank Street College of Education and at Teachers College, Columbia University, where she earned her doctorate. She has lived and taught in Tanzania, East Africa, and in Guatemala, Central America. She now lives in the Cascade mountains in Washington State with her husband and two daughters.

Authors and Storytellers

Aesop, credited with the original telling of "The Lion and the Mouse," as well as many other fables, was a Greek slave who lived about 600 B.C. For many years, Aesop's fables were handed down orally from generation to generation. No one knows how many of the stories attributed to Aesop were actually composed by him.

Barlow, Genevieve, reteller of "The Search for the Magic Lake," collected many Latin American stories, which are published in her book *Latin American Tales*.

Belpré, Pura (1889–1982), teller of "The Parrot Who Wouldn't Say 'Cataño,'" was born in Puerto Rico. She later moved to New York City, where she worked as a librarian and told stories to children. When she looked for folk tales from Puerto Rico to read to them, she couldn't find any, so she began to write down folk tales she had heard as a child. Some of her books are *Ote: A Puerto Rican Folktale, The Dance of the Animals*, and *Once in Puerto Rico*.

Bowman, James Cloyd, is the author of "Pecos Bill Invents the Lariat." Bowman made folklore his hobby, collecting stories from many and varied sources. His books of folklore include *Tales of a Finnish Tupa, The Adventures of Paul Bunyan*, and *Pecos Bill: The Greatest Cowboy of All Time*, from which this Pecos Bill story was taken.

Bruchac, Joseph, teller of "Gluscabi and the Game Animals" and "The Storytelling Stone," is a poet, novelist, and storyteller. Born in the Adirondacks, Bruchac draws on the legends and myths of those mountains, as well as on his own Native American (Abenaki) ancestry.

Bryan, Ashley, teller of "The Dancing Granny," was born in New York City. His parents came from the island of Antigua. He was formerly a professor at Dartmouth College. Bryan now has a studio on Little Cranberry Island in Maine. He has written, compiled, and illustrated many books, including *The Ox of the Wonderful Horns and Other African Folktales; Beat the Story Drum, Pum-Pum*; and *The Cat's Purr*.

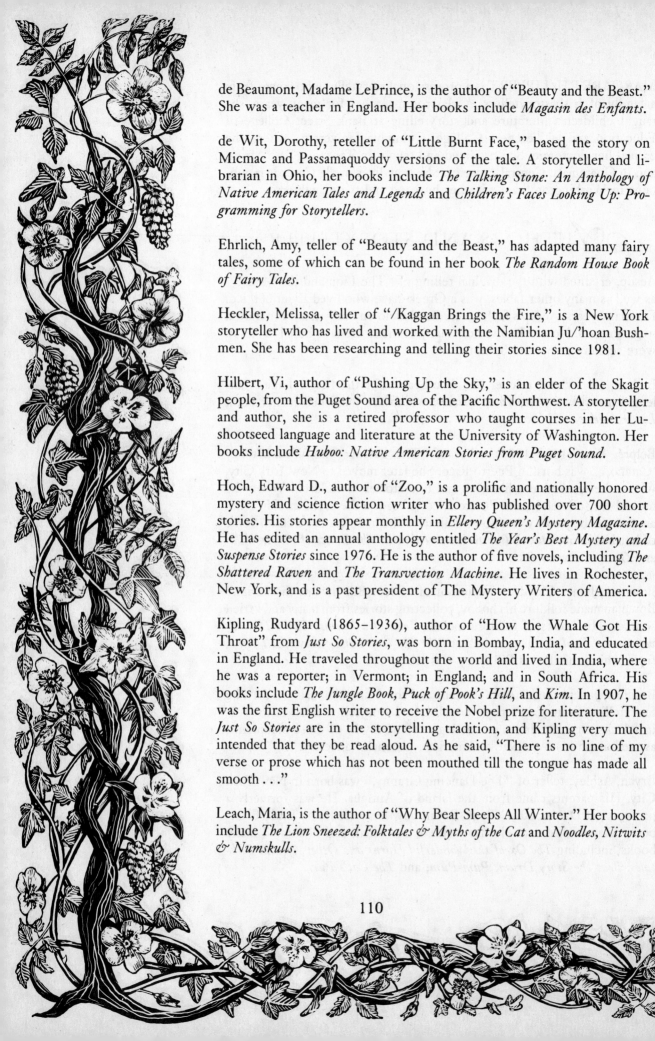

de Beaumont, Madame LePrince, is the author of "Beauty and the Beast." She was a teacher in England. Her books include *Magasin des Enfants*.

de Wit, Dorothy, reteller of "Little Burnt Face," based the story on Micmac and Passamaquoddy versions of the tale. A storyteller and librarian in Ohio, her books include *The Talking Stone: An Anthology of Native American Tales and Legends* and *Children's Faces Looking Up: Programming for Storytellers*.

Ehrlich, Amy, teller of "Beauty and the Beast," has adapted many fairy tales, some of which can be found in her book *The Random House Book of Fairy Tales*.

Heckler, Melissa, teller of "/Kaggan Brings the Fire," is a New York storyteller who has lived and worked with the Namibian Ju/'hoan Bushmen. She has been researching and telling their stories since 1981.

Hilbert, Vi, author of "Pushing Up the Sky," is an elder of the Skagit people, from the Puget Sound area of the Pacific Northwest. A storyteller and author, she is a retired professor who taught courses in her Lushootseed language and literature at the University of Washington. Her books include *Huboo: Native American Stories from Puget Sound*.

Hoch, Edward D., author of "Zoo," is a prolific and nationally honored mystery and science fiction writer who has published over 700 short stories. His stories appear monthly in *Ellery Queen's Mystery Magazine*. He has edited an annual anthology entitled *The Year's Best Mystery and Suspense Stories* since 1976. He is the author of five novels, including *The Shattered Raven* and *The Transvection Machine*. He lives in Rochester, New York, and is a past president of The Mystery Writers of America.

Kipling, Rudyard (1865–1936), author of "How the Whale Got His Throat" from *Just So Stories*, was born in Bombay, India, and educated in England. He traveled throughout the world and lived in India, where he was a reporter; in Vermont; in England; and in South Africa. His books include *The Jungle Book, Puck of Pook's Hill*, and *Kim*. In 1907, he was the first English writer to receive the Nobel prize for literature. The *Just So Stories* are in the storytelling tradition, and Kipling very much intended that they be read aloud. As he said, "There is no line of my verse or prose which has not been mouthed till the tongue has made all smooth . . ."

Leach, Maria, is the author of "Why Bear Sleeps All Winter." Her books include *The Lion Sneezed: Folktales & Myths of the Cat* and *Noodles, Nitwits & Numskulls*.

110

Newell, Edythe W., author of "The Boy Who Caught the Wind," was born in Oregon. She was a librarian in a public elementary school in Fairbanks, Alaska, and wrote a collection of stories entitled *The Rescue of the Sun and Other Tales From the Far North*.

Paye, Won-Ldy, teller of "The Contest," is from the Dan people of Liberia, where he was raised in a family of Griots—village storytellers and historians. In addition to being a storyteller, drummer, and actor, he now directs a performing arts group in Seattle.

Rose, Deborah Lee, is the author of "The People Who Hugged the Trees." She is a science writer at the University of California at Berkeley.

Sandburg, Carl (1878–1967), is the author of "The Haystack Cricket and How Things Are Different Up in the Moon Towns," which is from his book entitled *Rootabaga Stories*. Sandburg twice won the Pulitzer Prize, for his monumental biography of Abraham Lincoln in 1940 and for his *Complete Poems* in 1950. He grew up in Galesburg, Illinois, left school at the age of 13, and traveled throughout the United States, taking jobs as a milkman, ice-harvester, dishwasher, fireman, and journalist.

Schoeman, P. J., who collected "/Kaggan Brings the Fire," is a South African writer. He traveled with South African Bushmen and published their stories as part of his account of his travels with them.

Thayer, Ernest Lawrence (1863–1940), the author of "Casey at the Bat," was born in Lawrence, Massachusetts. He was an essayist and a poet. He worked as a journalist for the *San Francisco Examiner*.

Thompson, Stith (1885–1976), teller of "The Theft of Fire," was an author, educator, and folklorist. He was a Distinguished Service Professor of English and Folklore at Indiana University. His books include *The Folktale*, *Round the Levee*, *One Hundred Favorite Folktales*, *Tales of the North American Indians*, and the six volume *Motif-Index of Folk Literature*.

Turnbull, Lucia, reteller of "The Mouse Bride," collected other fairy tales from India, which she published in her book *Fairy Tales of India*.

Uchida, Yoshiko, teller of "The Sea of Gold," won the Commonwealth Club of California Award for *Samurai of Gold Hill* in 1972. In addition to several collections of Japanese folk tales, she has also written *The Birthday Visitor*, *The Full Circle*, and *Jar of Dreams*.

Wilder, Laura Ingalls (1867–1957), is the author of "The Wolf-Pack," a chapter from *Little House on the Prairie*. She is best known for her series of nine novels called *The Little House Books*. Wilder based most of the series on her experiences growing up in the pioneer Midwest in the late 1800s.

INDEX

Index of Literature by Origin

Author and Storyteller Index

INDEX OF TITLES

Acknowledgments

The publisher gratefully acknowledges permission to reprint the following copyrighted material:

American Museum of Natural History
"The Theft of Fire" by Stith Thompson from BULLETIN OF THE AMERICAN MUSEUM OF NATURAL HISTORY, xvii, 65, No. 5. Reprinted by permission from American Museum of Natural History.

Atheneum Publishers
THE DANCING GRANNY by Ashley Bryan. Copyright © 1977 by Ashley Bryan. Reprinted with permission of Atheneum Publishers, an imprint of Macmillan Publishing Company.

Genevieve Barlow
"The Search for the Magic Lake" from LATIN AMERICAN TALES by Genevieve Barlow. Copyright © 1966 by Genevieve Barlow. Reprinted by permission of the author.

Dorothy de Wit
"Little Burnt Face" from THE TALKING STONE by Dorothy de Wit. Copyright © 1979 by Dorothy M. de Wit. Reprinted by permission of Adrian de Wit, for Estate of Dorothy de Wit.

Harcourt Brace Jovanovich
"The Haystack Cricket and How Things Are Different Up in the Moon Towns" from ROOTABAGA STORIES, Part Two, by Carl Sandburg. Copyright © 1923 by Harcourt Brace Jovanovich, Inc. Copyright © renewed 1951 by Carl Sandburg. Reprinted by permission of the publisher.

HarperCollins Publishers
"The Wolf Pack" from LITTLE HOUSE ON THE PRAIRIE by Laura Ingalls Wilder. Text Copyright © 1935 by Laura Ingalls Wilder. Copyright © renewed 1963 by Roger L. MacBride. Reprinted by permission of HarperCollins Publishers.

Melissa Heckler
"/Kaggan Brings the Fire" by Melissa Heckler. Copyright © 1991 by Melissa Heckler. Reprinted by permission of the author.

Vi (ṭaqʷ šəblu) Hilbert
"Pushing Up the Sky" by Vi (ṭaqʷ šəblu) Hilbert. One of the original tellers of this story was Chief William Shelton of the Tulalip Tribe (Lushootseed Territory, Washington State) in 1923. Copyright © 1991 by Lushootseed Research. Reprinted by permission of Vi (ṭaqʷ šəblu) Hilbert.

Barbara Kouts, Literary Agent
"The Storytelling Stone" and "Gluscabi and the Game Animals" from KEEPERS OF THE EARTH: *Native American Stories and Environmental Activities for Children* by Michael J. Caduto and Joseph Bruchac. Copyright © 1988, 1989 by Michael J. Caduto and Joseph Bruchac. Published by Fulcrum Press. Reprinted by permission of Barbara Kouts, literary agent for Joseph Bruchac.

Las Americas
"The Parrot Who Wouldn't Say 'Cataño'" from ONCE IN PUERTO RICO by Pura Belpré. Copyright © 1973 Pura Belpré. Used by permission of Las Americas.

Margaret H. Lippert
"The Lion and the Mouse," an Aesop fable retold by Margaret H. Lippert. Copyright © 1986 by Margaret H. Lippert. Used by permission of the author.

William Morrow and Company, Publishers
"Little Burnt Face" from THE TALKING STONE by Dorothy de Wit. Copyright © 1979 by Dorothy de Wit. Published by Greenwillow Books and reprinted by permission of William Morrow and Company, Publishers, New York.

Edythe W. Newell
"The Boy Who Caught the Wind" from THE RESCUE OF THE SUN *And Other Tales from the Far North* by Edythe W. Newell. Copyright © 1970 by Edythe W. Newell. Reprinted by permission of the author.

Won-Ldy Paye
"The Contest" by Won-Ldy Paye. Copyright © 1991 by Won-Ldy Paye. Used with permission of the author.

Penguin Books USA Inc.
"Why Bear Sleeps All Winter" from HOW THE PEOPLE SANG THE MOUNTAINS UP by Maria Leach. Copyright © 1967 by Maria Leach. Used by permission of Viking Penguin, a division of Penguin Books USA Inc.

Random Century Group
"The Mouse Bride" from FAIRY TALES OF INDIA by Lucia Turnbull. Published by Frederick Muller Ltd. Copyright © 1967 by Faber and Faber. Reprinted by permission of Random Century Group.

Random House, Inc.
"Beauty and the Beast" from THE RANDOM HOUSE BOOK OF FAIRY TALES adapted by Amy Ehrlich. Copyright © 1985 by Amy Ehrlich. Reprinted by permission of Random House, Inc.

Roberts Rinehart, Inc. Publishers
THE PEOPLE WHO HUGGED THE TREES: *An Environmental Folk Tale* adapted by Deborah Lee Rose from a story of Rajasthan, India. Copyright © 1990 by Deborah Lee Rose. Reprinted by permission of Roberts Rinehart, Inc. Publishers, P.O. Box 666, Niwot, CO 80544.

Larry Sternig Literary Agency
"Zoo" from YOUNG EXTRATERRESTRIALS by Edward D. Hoch. Copyright © 1958 Fantastic Universe SF. Reprinted by permission of Larry Sternig Literary Agency.

Yoshiko Uchida
"The Sea of Gold" from THE SEA OF GOLD AND OTHER TALES FROM JAPAN by Yoshiko Uchida. Copyright © 1965 by Yoshiko Uchida. Used by permission of the author.

Albert Whitman & Company
"Pecos Bill Invents the Lariat" was originally entitled "Pecos Bill Invents Modern Cowpunching" in PECOS BILL, THE GREATEST COWBOY OF ALL TIMES by James Cloyd Bowman. Copyright © 1937, 1964 by Albert Whitman & Company. All rights reserved. Used with permission of Albert Whitman & Company.

Cover Illustration: Scott McKowen

Cover Design: Carbone Smolan Associates

Illustration Credits: Gil Ashby, 66, 67; Pearl Beach, 73-75; Joe Boddy, 79-81; Circa 86, Inc., 43, 47-52, 103-108; Gretchen Geser, 84-86; James Grasow, 45, 46; Carol Greger, 43, 44; Janet Hamlin, 16-23, 47-52; Richard Leonard, 60-62, 87; Kelly Maddox, 2-15, 63-65, 109-115; Leonid Mysakov, 98-102; Vilma Ortiz, 92, 95; Nisa Rauschenberg, 82, 83; Lauren Rosenblum, 68-72, 89-91; Joanna Roy, 34-42, 76-78; Susan Swan, 26-33; Mary Thelen, 96, 97; Jean and Mou-Sien Tseng, 53-57; Yemi, 24, 25, 58, 59.

PLAYS **AND** CHORAL READINGS

CORRELATIONS
UNIT THEMES, PLAYS, AND CHORAL READINGS

LEVEL 10
Each play and choral reading selection has
been developed to reinforce the unit theme
in the Student Anthology

UNIT 1/Make a Wish

Theme: Wishes can bring unexpected results.

Play: *All the Money in the World* — a humorous play that illustrates some
of the unexpected consequences of literally getting what you wish for

Choral Reading: *Wish I May* and *White Horses* — poems about wishes

UNIT 2/Naturally!

Theme: The world of nature holds many mysteries and wonders.

Play: *Whodunit? Woo Knows* . . . — a mystery play that pits a clever thief
against an eleven-year-old sleuth and her remarkable parrot

Choral Reading: *Little Talk* and *But I Wonder* . . . — poems that raise
questions about insect life

UNIT 3/That's What Friends Are For

Theme: Friendships are built on cooperation, loyalty, and trust.

Play: *Nat Love, Western Hero* — a biographical play about the life and friendships of one of America's most famous black cowboys

Choral Reading: *The Question* and *Friend* — poems celebrating the joys of friendship

UNIT 4/Pitch In!

Theme: We're all responsible for preserving our planet and protecting its creatures.

Play: *The Nightingale* — a dramatization of a Hans Christian Andersen tale that points out the folly of trying to replace something natural with something artificial

Choral Reading: *And They Lived Happily Ever After for a While* — a whimsical poem about love in the midst of ecological disaster

UNIT 5/Memories to Keep

Theme: Keeping memories alive can help us today and tomorrow.

Play: *The Camera in the Attic* — a time-travel play in which three children are transported back to 1875 to experience history firsthand

Choral Reading: *So Will I* and *door* — poems about grandparents and memories

UNIT 6/Twice-Told Tales

Theme: Stories keep alive the wisdom and humor of a people from one generation to another.

Play: *Billy Beg and the Bull* — a dramatization of an Irish folk tale with a unique twist on the Cinderella theme

Choral Reading: *Look, Cinderella!* and *. . . And Then the Prince Knelt Down and Tried to Put the Glass Slipper on Cinderella's Foot* — poems offering some advice to modern-day Cinderellas

INTRODUCTION

We read for many different reasons, but chief among them should be the discovery that reading can be both fun and purposeful. And what could be more entertaining than working together to make words come alive in a Readers Theater or choral-reading presentation? This book of plays and choral readings has been developed to give you and your students an opportunity to enjoy reading aloud together. At the same time, your students will be developing their reading fluency skills through these enjoyable and motivating oral-reading experiences.

The following pages provide a compilation of hints and tips gathered from teachers who have made oral-reading techniques work in their classrooms. Unlike dramatic productions requiring memorization, elaborate sets, costumes, and stage directions, Readers Theater and choral reading only require a set of scripts and a group of enthusiastic readers—the former you are holding, while the latter wait in the wings of your classroom!

READERS THEATER—A DESCRIPTION

Readers Theater has been used by teachers for many years. Also known as Dramatic Reading, Chamber Theater, or Story Theater, the name Readers Theater seems most appropriate because it puts the emphasis where it belongs—on the *reading* rather than the memorization of a script. Unlike traditional drama in which performers memorize lines and move about a stage, Readers Theater is simply the rehearsed oral reading of a script by a group of performers. It requires no training in drama or the performing arts on the part of students or teachers; there are no complicated guidelines to follow. While simple costumes or backdrops can be used to help establish characterization and setting, they are optional. The fact that Readers Theater involves such simple techniques makes it a viable option for every classroom.

READERS THEATER AND CHORAL READING—THE BENEFITS

Among the chief benefits of Readers Theater and choral reading is the development of oral-reading fluency. Identified by some reading authorities as a frequently "neglected goal" of reading instruction, fluency training has been recognized as an important aspect of proficient reading.

Two essential components for successful fluency training are repeated reading and active listening. Most students can sharpen their active listening skills by attending while the teacher reads aloud for a brief period every day. However, convincing students to repeatedly read the same selection orally until fluency is achieved is quite a different matter. Usually the response is less than enthusiastic.

Enter Readers Theater and choral reading!— both natural partners for fluency training. The oral reading of plays and poetry generates a natural excitement and a willingness to rehearse that enables teachers to integrate repeated reading practice into their instructional program. The goal of a polished performance is a genuinely motivating force that provides a rationale for the fluency training that all students need. Readers Theater and choral reading offer students a *meaningful* context in which to practice expression, shading, phrasing, diction, pitch, and rate, as well as word recognition skills. (For additional information on fluency training and its benefits, see the articles listed in the Bibliography.)

Readers Theater and choral reading also develop active listening skills on the part of both participants and audience. Readers must listen attentively to pick up on cues or to chime in as a member of a group. Audience members also are encouraged to sharpen listening skills as they interpret the dialog and narration to visualize settings and characters that are described rather than visibly presented on stage.

In addition to developing fluency skills, Readers Theater and choral reading can also help students internalize literature, thereby improving their comprehension. Dramatizations enable readers to

Baa Baa Baa

"become" the characters they play. What better way to reinforce character and plot development than through plays? Dramatizations also expose students to the rich heritage of oral language and storytelling. Through the oral reading of scripts and poetry, students internalize the rhythm of repeated refrains, certain language conventions, and traditional story structure.

A final benefit of Readers Theater and choral reading is derived from the high levels of student interaction and involvement within cooperative learning groups. Through these shared oral-reading experiences, students learn to work together, take turns, listen to each other, and employ group decision-making and problem-solving strategies in casting and production decisions.

Unlike many group activities in which all participants must function on or about the same level to effectively complete the task, a Readers Theater group using the scripts in this book can be composed of students with widely differing reading abilities. The scripts have been written to include roles of varying length and difficulty, enabling students of all ability levels to fully participate and contribute to the achievement of the common goal: a shared oral-reading experience.

LAUNCHING READERS THEATER IN YOUR CLASSROOM

As the following steps indicate, introducing Readers Theater to your class is a straightforward procedure. The only rules are: Keep it simple! and Keep it fun!

1. SCRIPT PREPARATION

Decide when you want to introduce the Readers Theater play within a unit. Then duplicate a copy of the script for each cast member and the director. (Since scripts sometimes have a habit of disappearing, you might make a few extras, just in case.) Students can make construction-paper covers, using the full-page art that precedes each script for decoration, if they wish.

2. ROLE ASSIGNMENT

The plays in this collection were purposefully written with roles requiring varying levels of reading proficiency. Initially you may want to take into account individual reading ability when making role assignments, but once students have become familiar with a play, roles can and should be switched. Because the characters are read rather than acted, the part of a boy can be read by a girl and vice versa. As students become familiar with Readers Theater, they should be encouraged to assume responsibility for casting decisions as they participate within the cooperative decision-making environment of a Readers Theater group.

3. REHEARSALS

In the first rehearsal, students in the cast should sit together in a Readers Theater group—perhaps gathered around a table—and read through the script to get a sense of the plot and characters. If the play is an adaptation, you may want to read aloud the original story. (Sources for stories that have been adapted appear in the Bibliography.) At this time, roles should be assigned or agreed upon, and students can be encouraged to identify their lines with a transparent highlighter.

Subsequent rehearsals should include paired repeated readings where two characters rehearse their lines together. Having a tape recorder available for these readings will enable students to evaluate their progress. In these early rehearsals, students should focus on word recognition and on listening for cues. Once these goals have been achieved, attention can be turned to articulation, expression, rate, shading, and phrasing. Invite students to make "reader's notes" in pencil in their scripts. A slash, for example, can be used as a reminder of a pause not indicated by punctuation. An underline can indicate that a word needs special emphasis. These notations can be a valuable aid to oral reading.

During rehearsals, students may decide to add their own personal touches to a script. If the cast decides to add, delete, or alter a speech, this change should be made in all copies of the script.

Macmillan/McGraw-Hill

4. BLOCKING AND FOCUS

In Readers Theater, the performers usually do not move about the stage. However, there are two bits of "stage business" that require rehearsal—where the performers will sit in relation to each other, and where they should look when they are speaking.

Each play is accompanied by a blocking diagram that suggests a seating arrangement. Before the performance, students will need to practice entering, assuming their places on stools or chairs, and exiting. If music stands are available, you may wish to have students use them to hold their scripts during a performance. In some cases, a music stand for the narrator has been suggested in the blocking diagram.

Focus should be an important part of the rehearsal process because, with the exception of a simple gesture or two, focus is the only direct action employed during a Readers Theater presentation. Basically, there are two kinds of focus that students can use: on-stage and off-stage focus. In on-stage focus, the characters look at each other when they speak. In off-stage focus, the characters direct their gaze to a spot on the wall behind the audience. In both types of focus, it is important that students be familiar enough with their lines so their eyes and heads are up rather than buried in a script.

5. PROPS AND COSTUMES

While elaborate costumes and props are not necessary for Readers Theater, even the simplest costumes, such as hats, scarves, or animal ears can help students assume their character. Costume suggestions can be found on the resource pages following several of the plays.

Making background murals or very simple props can help students deepen their understanding of a play. Involvement in discussions about what to emphasize in a drawing or in the scenery or about which free-standing props would suggest the setting (a tree) or occasion (a birthday cake) allows a further involvement and commitment on the part of participants. Either the performers or another group of students acting as stage crew can create the props and costumes.

Hand-held props are not suggested for Readers Theater because the hands should be free to hold the script. For a similar reason, masks should be avoided since they may impair the performers' ability to see the script or project the lines.

6. THE STAGE

Readers Theater does not require a proscenium stage with a curtain, just an open area with enough space for the cast and an audience. A corner of the classroom will work as well as the school auditorium. For plays that lend themselves to puppet dramatizations, simple directions for both the puppets and the stage are included in the resource pages. In staging a Readers Theater puppet show, it generally works best to have one cast read the script while another cast operates the puppets.

7. SHARING THE PERFORMANCE

Readers Theater presentations are meant to be shared, but the audience can range from one person to a packed auditorium. Before the performance begins, you or a student may wish to briefly introduce the conventions of Readers Theater so that the audience understands its role in interpreting dialog to visualize the characters and the action. Students may enjoy making programs, tickets, and posters for the production, especially if another class or parents are invited to attend. On the day of the performance, have the characters enter, take their places, and read!

8. PERFORMANCE FOLLOW-UP

After the performance, suggest that the cast gather to discuss their reading of the play. To guide their discussion, they may use the Self-Evaluation Form. By assessing their own performances as readers, as listeners, and as group members, students can set personal goals to work toward during their next oral-reading experience.

WRITE YOUR OWN READERS THEATER PLAY

After participating in a Readers Theater performance, some students will be eager to write their own plays. The Write Your Own Readers Theater Play resource pages have been designed to guide students through this process.

The teacher resource page presents an overview of the steps and highlights some of the major differences between narrative and drama. Once students understand those differences, they can work with partners or in small groups to complete the student resource pages.

- *Getting Started* guides students in answering the question, "How do I get an idea for a play?"

- *The Plot* defines plot structure and gives a model of a plot outline. Building on the previous worksheet, students develop their own plot outline based on one of the play ideas previously identified.

- *Creating a Character* discusses methods for developing realistic characters and models how to write character sketches.

- *A Readers Theater Script* illustrates the proper format for a script. Additionally, it focuses attention on key questions involving the role of the narrator and the importance of creating dialog consistent with a character sketch.

- *Ready, Set, Write!* is a writing-process checklist to help students keep track of the steps involved in prewriting, drafting, revising, proofreading, and publishing a Readers Theater play.

THE CHORAL READING EXPERIENCE

Choral reading, like Readers Theater, is an activity that promotes fluency through cooperative effort. In choral reading, speaking and listening are complementary processes—groups of students practice reading poetry for another group to listen to. During practice sessions, the group will need a director, usually the teacher in the early sessions. As students become more experienced with this technique, they can explore taking on the responsibilities of the director.

TYPES OF CHORAL READING

Choral reading promotes fluency by giving support to readers, by providing an opportunity for repeated reading with special attention to rhythm and meter, and by encouraging active listening. The four major types of choral reading are

- refrain
- antiphonal
- line-by-line
- unison

In a poem with a refrain, the verse can be read by a solo voice, by a group (the most common choice), or in combination. In line-by-line choral reading, each line or group of lines is read by a different group or solo voice. Antiphonal choral readings are somewhat like call and response, with one group answering another. Unison readings—perhaps the most difficult of all—are read by the entire group.

The choral readings for each unit have suggestions for groups and solo voices. Your students should first try reading the poems as arranged. After they are familiar with a particular reading, encourage them to try other arrangements or other poems.

SIZE AND ORGANIZATION OF THE CHORAL READING GROUP

You and your students may want to experiment with the size of the choral reading group, which will vary depending upon the number of students who want to participate and the particular piece being performed. Most often, members of a group should stand together. Sometimes, readers with solo parts are also part of a group. In these cases, the soloists should stand in the front row of the group. Resource pages suggest arrangements of speakers for choral reading.

THE RESOURCE PAGES

This book includes both teacher and student resource pages. Resource pages follow the plays and always include a blocking diagram for the play. Other resource pages may include costume suggestions and patterns, a pronunciation guide, prop suggestions, puppets, puppet-show directions, sound effects, and audiotaping instructions for radio plays. Resource pages for the choral readings include blocking diagrams. The final resource page is a self-evaluation form for readers and listeners.

BIBLIOGRAPHY

ARTICLES ON READING FLUENCY

ALLINGTON, R.L. 1983. Fluency: The neglected reading goal. *The Reading Teacher* 36:556-61.

BEAVER, J.M. 1982. Say it! Over and over. *Language Arts* 59:143-48.

DOWHOWER, S.L. 1987. Effects of repeated reading on second-grade transitional readers' fluency and comprehension. *Reading Research Quarterly* 22:389-406.

_____ . 1989. Repeated reading: Research into practice. *The Reading Teacher* 42:502-7.

KOSKINEN, P.S., and I.H. BLUM. 1986. Paired repeated reading: A classroom strategy for developing fluent reading. *The Reading Teacher* 40:70-75.

MICCINATI, J.L. 1985. Using prosodic cues to teach oral reading fluency. *The Reading Teacher* 39:206-12.

RASINSKI, T. 1989. Fluency for everyone: Incorporating fluency instruction in the classroom. *The Reading Teacher* 42:690-93.

_____ , and J.B. ZUTELL. 1990. Making a place for fluency instruction in the regular reading curriculum. *Reading Research and Instruction* 29:85-91.

SAMUELS, S.J. 1988. Decoding and automaticity: Helping poor readers become automatic at word recognition. *The Reading Teacher* 41:756-60.

ARTICLES ON READERS THEATER AND DRAMATIC READING

ANDERSEN, D.R. 1987. Around the world in eighty days. *Instructor* 97(October): 62-63.

_____ . 1989. The shy exclamation point. *Instructor* 98(February): 54.

_____ . 1988. The sound of great voices. *Instructor* 97(January): 46-47.

BENNETT, S., and K. BEATTY. 1988. Grades 1 and 2 love readers theatre. *The Reading Teacher* 41:485.

BIDWELL, S.M. 1990. Using drama to increase motivation, comprehension and fluency. *Journal of Reading* 34:38-41.

BURNS, G., and E. KIZER. 1987. Audio-visual effects in readers' theatre: A case study. *International Journal of Instructional Media* 14(3): 223-37.

DICKINSON, E. 1987. Readers Theatre: A creative method to increase reading fluency and comprehension skills. *The New England Reading Association Journal* 23(22): 7-11.

EPPERHEIMER, D. 1991. Readers' Theatre and technology: A perfect mix. *The California Reader* 24(Spring): 14-15.

FREEDMAN, M. 1990. Readers Theatre: An exciting way to motivate reluctant readers. *The New England Reading Association Journal* 26(Autumn): 9-12.

HOWARD, W.L., and others. 1989. Using choral responding to increase active student response. *Teaching Exceptional Children*. 21(Spring): 72-75.

NAVASCUES, M. 1988. Oral and dramatic interpretation of literature in the Spanish class. *Hispania* 71(March): 186-89.

STEWIG, J.W. 1990. Children's books for readers' theatre. *Perspectives* Spring:vii-x.

BOOKS ON READERS THEATER

BAUER, CAROLINE FELLER. *Celebrations: Read-Aloud Holiday and Theme Book Programs*. New York: H.W. Wilson, 1985.

_____ . *Presenting Reader's Theatre: Plays and Poems to Read Aloud*. New York: H.W. Wilson, 1987.

COGER, LESLIE IRENE, and MELVIN R. WHITE. *Readers Theatre Handbook: A Dramatic Approach to Literature*. 3d ed. Glenview, Ill.: Scott, Foresman, 1982.

FORKERT, OTTO MAURICE. *Children's Theatre that Captures Its Audience*. Chicago: Coach House Press, 1962.

LAUGHLIN, MILDRED KNIGHT, and KATHY HOWARD LATROBE. *Readers Theatre for Children*. Englewood, Colo.: Teacher Ideas Press, 1990.

SIERRA, JUDY, and ROBERT KAMINSKI. *Twice Upon a Time: Stories to Tell, Retell, Act Out, and Write About*. New York: H.W. Wilson, 1989.

SLOYER, SHIRLEE. *Readers Theatre: Story Dramatization in the Classroom*. Urbana, Ill.: National Council of Teachers of English, 1982.

_____ . "Readers Theatre: A Reading Motivator." In *Selected Articles on the Teaching of Reading*. New York: Barnell Loft, 1977.

BOOKS ON CHORAL READING

AGGERTT, OTIS J., and ELBERT R. BOWEN. *Communicative Reading*. New York: Macmillan, 1972.

GOTTLIEB, MARVIN R. *Oral Interpretation*. New York: McGraw-Hill, 1980.

JOHNSON, ALBERT, and BERTHA JOHNSON. *Oral Reading: Creative and Interpretive*. South Brunswick: A. S. Barnes, 1971.

BOOKS ON COSTUMES, MAKE-UP, AND PROPS

ARNOLD, A. *Arts and Crafts for Children and Young People*. London: Macmillan, 1976.

BARWELL, EVE. *Disguises You Can Make*. New York: Lothrop, Lee & Shepard, 1977.

CHERNOFF, GOLDIE TAUB. *Easy Costumes You Don't Have to Sew*. New York: Four Winds Press, 1975.

HALEY, GAIL E. *Costumes for Plays and Playing*. New York: Metheun, 1982.

Make and Play Paperback Set (includes costumes, face painting, hats, masks, and T-shirt painting). New York: Franklin Watts, 1990.

McCASLIN, NELLIE. *Shows on a Shoestring: An Easy Guide to Amateur Productions*. New York: David McKay, 1979.

MORIN, ALICE. *Newspaper Theatre: Creative Play Production for Low Budgets and No Budgets*. Belmont, Calif.: Fearon Teacher Aids, 1989.

PARISH, PEGGY. *Costumes to Make*. New York: Macmillan, 1970.

PITCHER, CAROLINE, consultant. *Masks and Puppets*. New York: Franklin Watts, 1984.

PURDY, SUSAN. *Costumes for You to Make*. Philadelphia: J.B. Lippincott, 1971.

SOURCE FOR ADAPTATIONS

All the Money in the World, by Bill Brittain. New York: Harper & Row, 1979.

"Billy Beg and the Bull." From *Favorite Fairy Tales Told Around the World,* by Virginia Haviland. Boston: Little, Brown and Company, 1985.

The Nightingale, by Hans Christian Andersen. Illustrated by Lisbeth Zwerger. New York: Scholastic, 1991.

The Nightingale, by Hans Christian Andersen. Translated by Eve Le Gallienne. New York: HarperCollins Children's Books, 1985.

Macmillan/McGraw-Hill

ALL THE MONEY IN THE WORLD

BY RICHARD HOLLAND BASED ON THE NOVEL BY BILL BRITTAIN

·CAST·

NARRATOR	MR. STOWE	MR. MILLERIDGE
VINCENT ARBOR	MRS. STOWE	MRS. HOBSON
ROSELYNN PEABODY	PRESIDENT	MISS DRAYMORE
QUENTIN STOWE	GENERAL MAINWARING	MAYOR
FLAN	SERGEANT	MRS. TRUSSKER

·SETTING·

A small farming community

Macmillan/McGraw-Hill

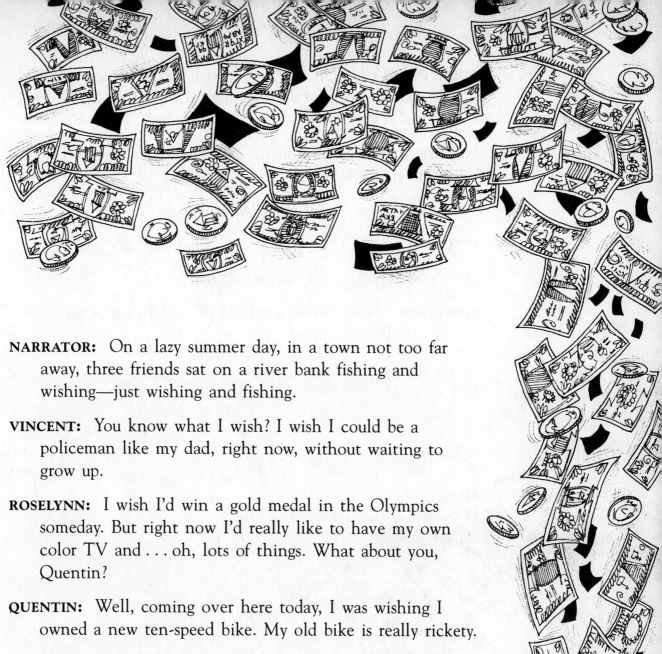

NARRATOR: On a lazy summer day, in a town not too far away, three friends sat on a river bank fishing and wishing—just wishing and fishing.

VINCENT: You know what I wish? I wish I could be a policeman like my dad, right now, without waiting to grow up.

ROSELYNN: I wish I'd win a gold medal in the Olympics someday. But right now I'd really like to have my own color TV and . . . oh, lots of things. What about you, Quentin?

QUENTIN: Well, coming over here today, I was wishing I owned a new ten-speed bike. My old bike is really rickety.

ROSELYNN: I'm glad my dad can't hear us talking this way. He says I spend too much time wishing for things.

VINCENT: That sounds just like my father. He says I do too much daydreaming and not enough homework. Do you get into trouble for daydreaming, Quentin?

QUENTIN: Yeah. At breakfast I wished I had ten dollars to spend any way I wanted. But when Poppa heard me, he said, "Stop all this foolishness. I don't want to hear any more talk about money."

ROSELYNN: Hey! Maybe that's why the three of us get along so well. Each of us can wish for whatever we want and know the other two won't laugh when we talk about it.

QUENTIN: Well, right now I just wish I could catch a really big fish so I could take it home for supper. Wait! I've got a bite! It's a big one!

ROSELYNN: Be careful, Quent! Don't pull too hard or you'll break the line!

QUENTIN: Okay . . . I'll be . . . careful.

VINCENT: Wow! Did you see that fish jump? It's huge!

QUENTIN: Help . . . me . . . pull it in!

ROSELYNN: Okay! We've got hold of you! Ready? One . . . two . . . three. . . . Pull!

Macmillan/McGraw-Hill

QUENTIN: We did it! Wow! It's the biggest bass I've ever seen! I'd better take it right home. See you later.

ROSELYNN: When?

QUENTIN: Let's all meet at my house this afternoon. I'll have my chores done by then.

VINCENT: Okay. So long.

NARRATOR: Quentin's wish to catch a big fish had come true. So as he pedaled home on his old, rusty bicycle, he wished for bigger things.

QUENTIN: I wish I had a ten-speed bike like Roselynn's . . . and a new coat for Momma . . . and a tractor that really ran right for Poppa. And maybe even . . .

NARRATOR: Just then there was a loud POP! Then a long *psssss*.

QUENTIN: Oh, no! Not another flat tire! By the time I get it fixed, this fish will spoil in the sun. Wait a minute, there's a well. Good! I'll put my fish in the bucket and drop the bucket into the water. That should keep it fresh.

FLAN: Hey, you up there! Don't drop that bucket on my head!

QUENTIN: Is somebody down there?

FLAN: I am! Now, are you going to help a poor old man or not?

QUENTIN: How far down are you?

FLAN: Since I'm standing up to my knees in water, I'd say I was on the bottom. Have you a rope or something?

QUENTIN: All I have is a fishing pole.

FLAN: Splendid. Just lower it down to me.

QUENTIN: The line is not very strong.

FLAN: You'd be surprised how little I weigh, lad. Just lower it down, and we'll make do.

QUENTIN: All right. Here it comes.

FLAN: I see it. . . . Just a bit farther. . . . Ah, I've got it. Haul away, lad!

QUENTIN: You *are* very light. Are you okay?

FLAN: You're doing fine. Another couple of feet and I'll be out.

NARRATOR: Quentin pulled up on his fishing pole until a hand grasped the side of the well. It was a tiny hand, no bigger than the hand of a doll. But, more amazing than the size was the color—it was *green*.

FLAN: That's it, lad, I'm out. The wet and the dark are more than a body should have to bear.

NARRATOR: Quentin was wide-eyed with wonder. It was a man, but one such as Quentin had never seen before. He was no bigger than a doll. His face, like his hands, was pale green and wrinkled with age. On his head, which was no bigger than a baseball, sat a tiny top hat. And in his teeth, he held the stem of a tiny pipe.

QUENTIN: Hello . . . sir. I'm Quentin Stowe. And you'd be . . . ?

FLAN: I'd best be on my way, thanking you very much for pulling me out of the well.

QUENTIN: Hey, wait! I saved your life. The least you can do is tell me who you are.

NARRATOR: Quentin's fishing pole gave a jerk—the silver hook was snagged in the man's coattails.

FLAN: I wonder if you'd be so kind as to take the hook out of my coattails, lad. It's hard to reach back there.

QUENTIN: I will, but first tell me who you are.

FLAN: No good will come of this, lad. But since you must know, I'm called Flan.

QUENTIN: Flan. That's an unusual name. What kind of a person are you, Mr. Flan?

FLAN: Not *mister*. Just plain Flan. I'm what folks call a leprechaun. I come from Ireland. Just what is it you're staring at?

QUENTIN: I never saw anybody with green skin before.

FLAN: Now don't go making fun of me because of my color. Green's just as good as black or white or purple or gold or whatever color skin comes in these days. Besides, what's another color between friends?

QUENTIN: You may be in for trouble. Poppa says that sometimes people with different skin colors don't get along too well together.

FLAN: The first person who tries something with me because of my color, I'll give *him* green skin, I will. I'll turn him into a frog.

QUENTIN: You can do that?

FLAN: If you know anything at all about leprechauns, you know we can do all sorts of magic.

QUENTIN: If you can do magic, why couldn't you get out of the well? Why did you need my help?

FLAN: Because I fell asleep in school during the lesson on flying. The lesson was terribly complicated, and the day was hot, and I was tired. I dozed off, and the result is that I can't fly. There was no way out of the well until you came along. Now, lad, you must claim your due.

QUENTIN: My due?

FLAN: You caught me fair and square, and you made me say my name. By the Law of the Leprechauns, I must grant you three wishes.

QUENTIN: Three wishes! Wow! Can I wish for anything?

FLAN: Anything at all. But I'd best warn you. Whatever you wish for, that's what you'll get. And you'll have it for all time.

QUENTIN: I guess I'd better think about this. But right now I'd better be getting home. Would you like to come along?

FLAN: Don't mind if I do. I was living in a cozy nook under a nice porch that belonged to a Mrs. Viola Trussker. But her singing got to be too much for me—such whooping and shrieking! I had to leave. Where do you live?

QUENTIN: Four miles from here. I wish my bike was fixed. Then we'd be home in no time.

NARRATOR: There was a rumble of thunder and the very air seemed to vibrate. Then suddenly, the bike's flat tire was filled with air.

FLAN: First wish granted. Hop aboard.

QUENTIN: That's not fair! That wasn't a real wish.

FLAN: I'm afraid it was, lad.

QUENTIN: I wish there was a way to keep from making wishes that I don't want to make.

FLAN: Easy as pie. We won't consider your third wish fully made until you count to three after you've made it.

QUENTIN: My third wish? What do you mean? What happened to the second one?

FLAN: You just had it, wishing not to make wishes you don't wish to wish. You have one wish left.

QUENTIN: But I . . . Oh my, this wish business is more complicated than I thought it would be.

FLAN: Give your last one careful thought. And don't forget to count to three afterward.

NARRATOR: There were so many things Quentin wanted. The new bike, the things for Momma and Poppa, money for . . . Money! That was it!

QUENTIN: I know! I wish . . . I wish for all the money in the world. One . . . two . . . THREE!

NARRATOR: For a moment there was only silence. Then there was a tremendous WHUMPH, followed by noises as if the sky were tearing apart. Finally, there was an eerie quiet.

FLAN: Open your eyes, Quentin. Your wish has been granted.

NARRATOR: Slowly Quentin opened his eyes. He saw fields and cows and birds, but no money.

QUENTIN: It was all just talk, wasn't it, Flan?

FLAN: I wouldn't trick you, lad. You wanted all the money in the world, and you've got it. But it's more than anyone can carry.

Macmillan/McGraw-Hill

NARRATOR: Disappointed, Quentin pedaled his bike slowly toward the farm. But when the house came into view, he could barely see it. There were huge mounds of something where his father's crops used to be. It was . . .

QUENTIN: All the money in the world!

NARRATOR: Yes, piles of money that almost touched the clouds! Quentin ran to the nearest pile and plunged his arms in up to his shoulders. He picked up wads of bills and tossed them into the air. There were dollars and Mexican pesos and English pounds and Indian rupees and Dutch guilders and German marks—so many different kinds of money.

QUENTIN: Money! Money! Money, money, money, moneeeeeeeeeey!

NARRATOR: Quentin tramped on mounds of gold and silver coins. Finally, he came to the fence at the edge of the road, where Flan was seated on the top rail. The little leprechaun was wearing a wide grin on his face.

FLAN: See, lad? I kept my promise, didn't I? Who's this now?

MR. STOWE: Quentin? What's going on here? What's all this stuff where the crops used to be?

QUENTIN: We've got something better than crops, Poppa. We've got all the money in the world!

MR. STOWE: And I suppose Cinderella is coming to dinner tonight. Quentin, when you start with this daydreaming business, I just don't want to listen.

QUENTIN: But it's true, Poppa. It really is!

MR. STOWE: All this paper can't be worth a hill of beans.

FLAN: It's worth what all the money in the world is worth to anyone who has it.

MR. STOWE: Who's that little green man?

NARRATOR: As Quentin and Flan told Mr. Stowe the story of what happened, Vincent and Roselynn arrived on their bicycles. They listened in silence. Then Vincent gave out a yell.

VINCENT: Wow! Oh, wow! Think of all the things you can buy!

QUENTIN: Think of all the things *we* can buy! Here, take all you want. You, too, Roselynn.

NARRATOR: Roselynn and Vincent grabbed handfuls of money and stuffed the bills into their pockets and into their shirts and socks and shoes. When they were through, they looked round, fat, and lumpy.

ROSELYNN: Oh, Quentin! Gee, thanks! This is wonderful.

NARRATOR: Vincent and Roselynn waddled out onto the road. As they did, PONG! PONG! They weren't fat or round or lumpy any more. All the money they had stuffed into their clothing sat in two neat piles on the side of the road.

VINCENT: My money! It's gone! All of it's gone!

ROSELYNN: So's mine! I bet Quentin told Flan to take it all back!

QUENTIN: Now wait a minute. I didn't!

VINCENT: You never really meant for us to have any of the money, did you, Quentin?

ROSELYNN: Come on, Vincent. Let's go. We can still have fun, just the *two* of us.

NARRATOR: Quentin was very unhappy. His best friends were mad at him, and his poppa was upset and worried. This money business wasn't going the way he had planned. Flan, Mr. Stowe, and Quentin went in the house to see Mrs. Stowe. They had to figure out what to do about all that money.

MRS. STOWE: What are all those piles where the crops used to be? And who is this little green man? Isn't he the cutest thing!

QUENTIN: It's all the money in the world, Momma.

MRS. STOWE: All the money in the world? It can't possibly be!

QUENTIN: It is, Momma. And this is Flan. He's a leprechaun, and he gave me the money.

MRS. STOWE: But where did it come from? And what are you going to do with it?

MR. STOWE: Those are very good questions. I have a feeling we'll find the answers on the news. Quentin, turn on the TV.

QUENTIN: Yes, Poppa. Wow! The President's on! He's making a speech.

PRESIDENT: Fellow citizens, today something happened that has never before occurred in our history—the whole money supply of Washington, D.C., has disappeared. We have reports of money missing from Fort Knox and other locations, as well. We don't know how this happened. Until we find the money, most government work will have to stop. The situation is serious—quite serious—but not hopeless. In the meantime, we are planning to negotiate some loans from our allies abroad.

MRS. STOWE: Quentin, how much money did you say was out there?

QUENTIN: All the money in the world.

PRESIDENT: I have appointed General Linus Mainwaring to locate the missing money. General, do you have anything to say?

GENERAL: Yes, sir, Mr. President. I just want to say this to whoever has that money: We're going to find you, mister. And when we do—watch out!

NARRATOR: For the next two days Quentin saw how his wish affected the entire town. No one had money to buy anything. Stores were closing. Food was spoiling on the shelves. People were very upset. Quentin sat on top of a pile of money wondering what to do. Flan just relaxed on Quentin's shoulder. Suddenly, there was a low rumble. Then off in the distance . . .

QUENTIN: Trucks! Lots of them, coming this way! Look on the sides of the trucks—it says United States Army!

NARRATOR: The trucks screeched to a halt and a uniformed man jumped out. He had row after row of medals on his chest. Quentin recognized him from TV. It was General Mainwaring! He was followed by his staff sergeant.

GENERAL: It's the money, all right, just where our observation planes spotted it. Sergeant, tell the troops to advance across the fence and surround the money.

SERGEANT: Advance across the fence and surround the money!

GENERAL: You! You with that green thing on your shoulder. What's your name? And how did all this money get here?

QUENTIN: My name is Quentin Stowe, sir. And this is Flan. He brought the money here.

GENERAL: I see. Well, I'm here on orders from the President of the United States. We will now proceed to load up the money. Sergeant! Load the trucks. Take the gold bars first.

SERGEANT: Load up the money! Take the gold bars first!

NARRATOR: The soldiers loaded three trucks full of gold bars. It took them half the day, gold being as heavy as it is. The trucks sagged under the weight of the bars.

GENERAL: Move the trucks out!

SERGEANT: Move the trucks out!

NARRATOR: The trucks pulled off the grass onto the road. PONG! PONG! PONG! The rear of each truck bounced up into the air, but when it came back down, the truck was no longer sagging.

SERGEANT: General, the gold . . . it's not in the trucks any more. It's gone!

QUENTIN: It's not gone, sir. It's over here in the field.

GENERAL: You mean the gold went back onto the farm?

QUENTIN: Yes, sir. The money keeps coming back.

GENERAL: Impossible! Sergeant, have the troops surround the farm! Nobody touches this money! Set up tents and make camp. We may be here awhile.

NARRATOR: Quentin's troubles went from bad to worse. Not only were all the people in town suffering because of his wish, but the United States Army was now living on his family's farm. He had to do something, but what?

QUENTIN: I know! I'll go shopping and spend some of my money. That way the store owners can keep their stores open.

NARRATOR: Quentin stuffed his pockets full of coins and twenty dollar bills. To his delight, the money stayed in his pockets when he left the farm. He headed toward town with Flan. His first stop was at Mr. Milleridge's Ice Cream Store.

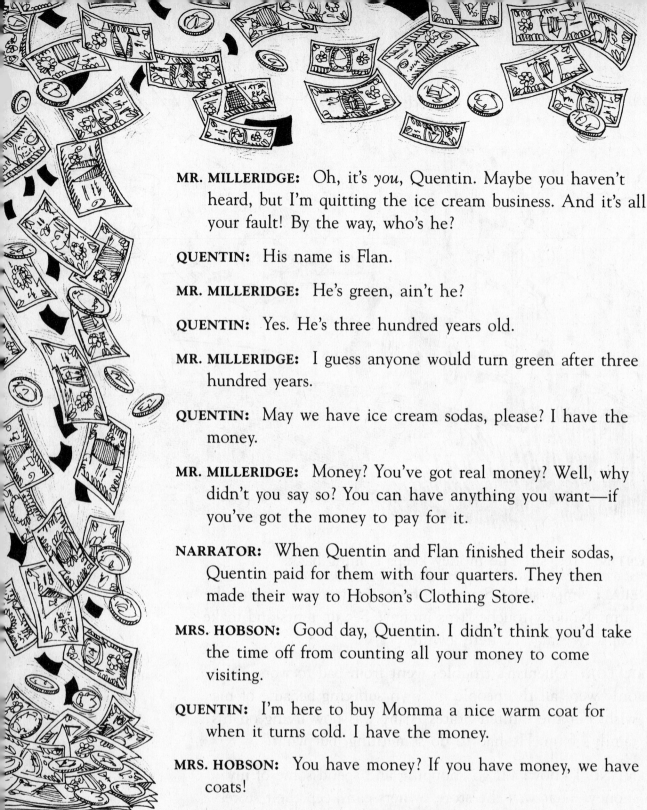

MR. MILLERIDGE: Oh, it's *you*, Quentin. Maybe you haven't heard, but I'm quitting the ice cream business. And it's all your fault! By the way, who's he?

QUENTIN: His name is Flan.

MR. MILLERIDGE: He's green, ain't he?

QUENTIN: Yes. He's three hundred years old.

MR. MILLERIDGE: I guess anyone would turn green after three hundred years.

QUENTIN: May we have ice cream sodas, please? I have the money.

MR. MILLERIDGE: Money? You've got real money? Well, why didn't you say so? You can have anything you want—if you've got the money to pay for it.

NARRATOR: When Quentin and Flan finished their sodas, Quentin paid for them with four quarters. They then made their way to Hobson's Clothing Store.

MRS. HOBSON: Good day, Quentin. I didn't think you'd take the time off from counting all your money to come visiting.

QUENTIN: I'm here to buy Momma a nice warm coat for when it turns cold. I have the money.

MRS. HOBSON: You have money? If you have money, we have coats!

NARRATOR: Mrs. Hobson took Quentin right to the best coats. She helped him pick out a coat that was thick and warm. Quentin gave her six twenty-dollar bills. Next stop was the jewelry store!

QUENTIN: Miss Draymore, I want a real nice watch for my father. I have the money right here.

Macmillan/McGraw-Hill

MISS DRAYMORE: Would you like a gold watch or a silver watch? Or maybe you would like one with jewels!

MRS. HOBSON: Stop! Don't sell him a thing! Quentin, you tricked us! The money you gave me has vanished!

MR. MILLERIDGE: Hold everything! Where is it? My money—where is it? You bought two sodas in my store. You paid for them with four quarters. No sooner were you out the door than the money was gone!

QUENTIN: Oh, no! The money's back in my pocket!

FLAN: The money's yours for all time. You can take it anywhere you'd like. But if you give it to someone else, you won't have all the money in the world any more. So it has to return to you.

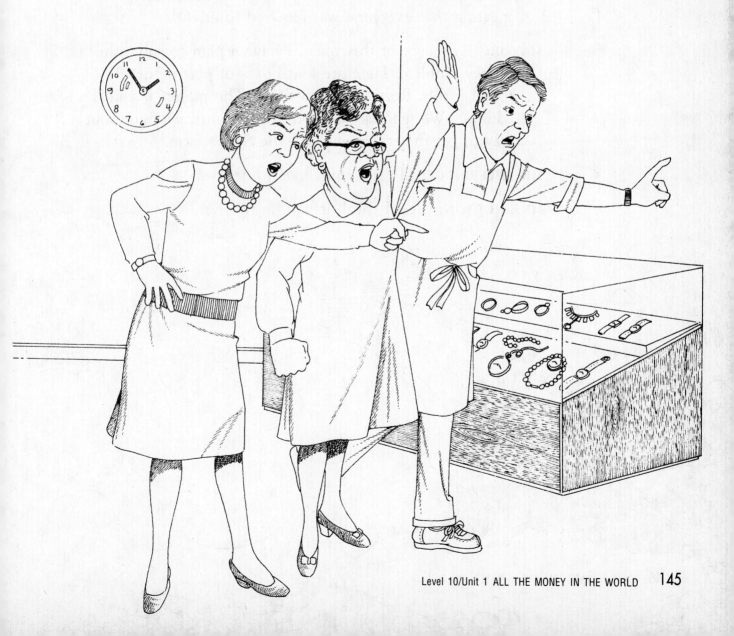

MISS DRAYMORE: No watch for you, young man!

MRS. HOBSON: And I will take back that coat, thank you very much!

MR. MILLERIDGE: Quentin, you and your green friend—follow me!

NARRATOR: Mr. Milleridge couldn't take his ice cream sodas back, so he made Quentin and Flan clean his basement. But Flan didn't think the mishap was his fault, so Quentin had to do all the cleaning himself.

QUENTIN: What good is having all the money in the world? I'm working twice as hard as I did when I had none!

NARRATOR: Quentin's idea to solve the money shortage didn't work out. So that evening, the mayor called a town meeting that everyone was required to attend.

MAYOR: As mayor of this town, I have a plan to solve the money problem. Here are four boxes of play money I found in Mr. Reese's Variety Store. The money is called "dillies." We will use dillies as money until we figure out a way to get the real money off the Stowe farm.

MR. MILLERIDGE: That sounds like a fine idea.

MRS. HOBSON: Yes, I think it will do nicely.

Macmillan/McGraw-Hill

MAYOR: Now, everyone who earns money get into line. Each of you will come up and tell me how much you earn in a week. Then I'll give you that much in dillies.

NARRATOR: The mayor handed out dilly bills until everyone in town was satisfied.

MAYOR: If anyone has any debts to pay off, this would be a good time to do it.

NARRATOR: There was a rustling of bills as people exchanged dilly money.

MAYOR: Now we're all settled up, and the town can get back to normal.

NARRATOR: That's what he thought. PONG! All the dillies appeared in Quentin's lap!

QUENTIN: Not again!

MR. MILLERIDGE: Quentin's got my dillies!

MRS. HOBSON: Mine, too!

FLAN: You fools, don't you see what has happened? You turned dillies into real money when you used them to pay off debts. Now that dillies are real money, they are part of all the money in the world. So Quentin gets them.

MR. MILLERIDGE: I want my dillies back!

NARRATOR: Just then, General Mainwaring stormed into the town meeting.

GENERAL: Attention! Quentin Stowe! You're coming with me. You have an appointment to keep—an appointment with the President of the United States.

NARRATOR: Quentin and Flan were rushed off to Washington, D.C., by helicopter. The President was waiting for them on the steps of the White House.

PRESIDENT: Hello, Quentin. Let's go to the Oval Office. It's the right place to discuss big problems, and today we have a very big problem on our hands. Quentin, why don't you just tell me how you came to have all that money.

NARRATOR: As they walked to the Oval Office, Quentin explained how it all started with his wishing for a ten-speed bicycle. Then he told about meeting Flan and his wish for all the money in the world and how it came true.

PRESIDENT: And now you can't wish the money away because you have no wishes left?

QUENTIN: That's right, Mr. President. And I can't even spend the money. It's been nothing but a big problem ever since I got it.

PRESIDENT: The problem is even bigger than you think. All the people of the world need things to live—things that take money to buy. But you have all the money.

QUENTIN: I'd give it all back if I could.

Macmillan/McGraw-Hill

PRESIDENT: I believe you would. But some countries think the United States is keeping the money on purpose. And because of that, they are threatening to declare war.

QUENTIN: War! They can't do that!

PRESIDENT: I'm afraid they not only can, Quentin, but they will. Flan, is there any way you can make the money go back to where it belongs?

FLAN: No, sir. He caught me and made me say my name. That's the only way a leprechaun grants wishes. Except . . . I'll say no more!

PRESIDENT: So there *is* a way for Quentin to get more wishes, isn't there, Flan? What is it? You *must* tell us!

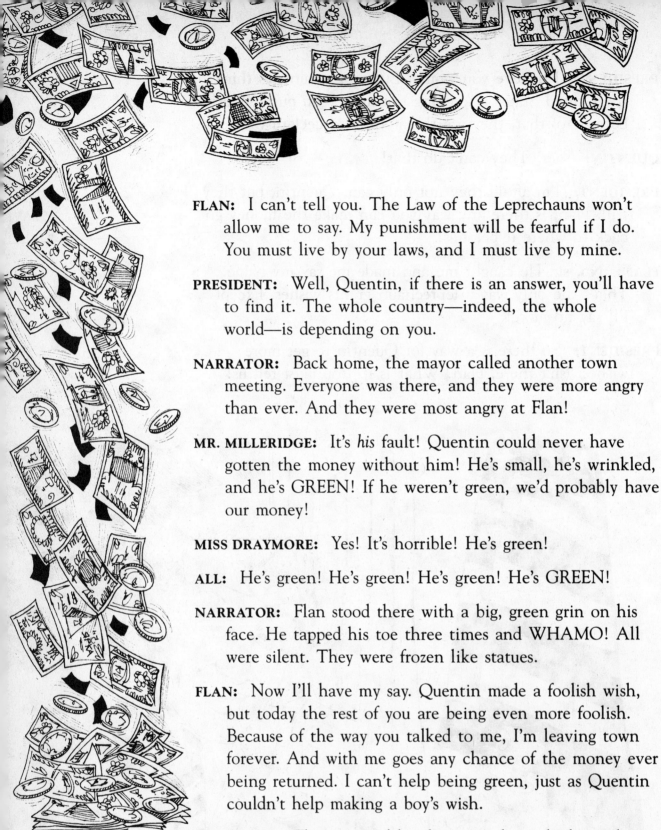

FLAN: I can't tell you. The Law of the Leprechauns won't allow me to say. My punishment will be fearful if I do. You must live by your laws, and I must live by mine.

PRESIDENT: Well, Quentin, if there is an answer, you'll have to find it. The whole country—indeed, the whole world—is depending on you.

NARRATOR: Back home, the mayor called another town meeting. Everyone was there, and they were more angry than ever. And they were most angry at Flan!

MR. MILLERIDGE: It's *his* fault! Quentin could never have gotten the money without him! He's small, he's wrinkled, and he's GREEN! If he weren't green, we'd probably have our money!

MISS DRAYMORE: Yes! It's horrible! He's green!

ALL: He's green! He's green! He's green! He's GREEN!

NARRATOR: Flan stood there with a big, green grin on his face. He tapped his toe three times and WHAMO! All were silent. They were frozen like statues.

FLAN: Now I'll have my say. Quentin made a foolish wish, but today the rest of you are being even more foolish. Because of the way you talked to me, I'm leaving town forever. And with me goes any chance of the money ever being returned. I can't help being green, just as Quentin couldn't help making a boy's wish.

NARRATOR: Flan snapped his fingers as he rushed out the door. Everyone was freed from the spell, and they rushed to follow him. Suddenly, from outside, they heard a loud CR-R-R-UNCH! Flan had fallen through a rotted-out section of the Town Hall steps, and now he was stuck up to his waist!

Macmillan/McGraw-Hill

FLAN: Don't anyone come near me! I'll change you all into caterpillars! Oh, fie on the day I slept through that flying lesson. Woe is me!

QUENTIN: You're stuck, Flan. Do you want me to help you get out?

FLAN: No, lad. I will not beg! So don't think I will.

NARRATOR: At that moment, Quentin was sure he knew Flan's secret.

QUENTIN: That's it! I can get three more wishes if you beg me to save you. Isn't that it, Flan?

FLAN: Not three more wishes, just one. But don't think I'll beg you, lad. Especially after the way you made a mess of your last wish.

QUENTIN: Then I'll just have to ask Mrs. Trussker to sing for you.

NARRATOR: Mrs. Trussker was the worst singer in the world. People said she could sour milk just by singing near a cow.

QUENTIN: Mrs. Trussker, Flan likes your singing very much. Could you please oblige him with a song?

MRS. TRUSSKER: Why, Quentin, it would be my pleasure. [*sings*]
Daisy, Daisy, give me your answer, do.
I'm half crazy, all for the love of yewww. . . .

FLAN: No, Quentin! It's cruel torture, that's what it is!

MRS. TRUSSKER: *It won't be a stylish marriage,*
I can't afford a carriage,
But you'll look sweet . . .

FLAN: Enough! Make her stop!

MRS. TRUSSKER: *Upon the seat*
Of a bicycle built for twooooooo!

FLAN: I give up, Quentin! I beg you to save me, and I'll grant you one more wish!

Macmillan/McGraw-Hill

NARRATOR: Quentin took Flan's hand and gently pulled him out of the hole in the steps.

FLAN: Make your wish quickly, lad. Then I'm leaving this town as fast as my legs will carry me.

NARRATOR: Quentin closed his eyes.

QUENTIN: I wish . . . for all the money in the world to go back to where it belongs. One . . . two . . . THREE!

NARRATOR: Quentin opened his eyes. The first thing he saw was Flan scurrying down the street. Then he heard . . .

MR. MILLERIDGE: It's money! Real money! Sixteen dollars and thirty-two cents, right here in my pocket!

MAYOR: The money's back in the bank! Piles and piles of it!

NARRATOR: Yes, the money was back in the banks and the houses and the pockets where it belonged. All the townspeople breathed a sigh of relief as they headed back to their homes and families. Happiest of all, Quentin went home and had his first good sleep in days. The next morning, he woke to the sight of the crops growing in the fields once again. As he finished up his chores, he looked up to find Vincent and Roselynn at the kitchen door, asking him to go fishing.

VINCENT: I'm sorry I acted the way I did, Quentin. Money makes people do funny things.

ROSELYNN: I'm sorry, too, Quentin. Money isn't as important as friends. And the three of us are best friends.

NARRATOR: Just then there was the rumble of a truck coming up the road. It was an army truck, and when it stopped, General Mainwaring jumped out.

QUENTIN: Oh, no! Not again! What's happened now?

NARRATOR: The sergeant hopped out of the back, pulling something big. He was smiling.

GENERAL: Quentin Stowe!

QUENTIN: Yes, sir?

GENERAL: The President sent me to tell you that he isn't little and he isn't green and he can't grant your every wish. But there is one thing he can grant you—a new ten-speed bicycle! It's the best that money can buy.

QUENTIN: Thank you, sir! Vincent! Roselynn! Let's go for a spin!

NARRATOR: The general saluted as the three friends rode away with their fishing poles. They were off for a day of fishing—yes, fishing, but not *too* much wishing.

BLOCKING DIAGRAM

Arrange fourteen chairs or stools, as shown. If possible, have the cast member reading the part of Flan sit on a low stool. The narrator can use a music stand to hold the script.

1. NARRATOR
2. FLAN
3. ROSELYNN PEABODY
4. VINCENT ARBOR
5. QUENTIN STOWE
6. MR. STOWE
7. MRS. STOWE
8. MAYOR

9. MRS. TRUSSKER
10. MR. MILLERIDGE
11. MISS DRAYMORE
12. MRS. HOBSON
13. GENERAL MAINWARING
14. SERGEANT
15. PRESIDENT

COSTUME SUGGESTIONS

Flan Flan's costume should consist of a green T-shirt, green pants, and green knee socks. For a leprechaun effect, the student playing Flan can tuck the pants legs into the knee socks and "blouse" them at the knee. A top hat can be added to complete the effect. The student can make one by following these directions. (1) Cut a long strip of six-inch-wide green construction paper. (2) Roll the strip into a cylinder. Adjust the circumference to fit your head, trim the excess paper, and staple or tape the cylinder at the seam. This will be the crown of the hat. (3) To make the brim, place the crown on a sheet of stiff green paper and trace around the base of the crown; then draw a larger circle around the first circle. On the inner circle, draw six or seven tabs. Cut the brim; then fold the tabs so that they stand upright. To attach the brim, glue the tabs to the inside of the crown.

Quentin, Roselynn, Vincent The performers can wear overalls, jeans, or shorts and may individualize their costumes by adding a bandanna or a straw hat.

Macmillan/McGraw-Hill

Mr. and Mrs. Stowe Quentin's parents should be dressed like farmers—in overalls or jeans and work shirts. The student playing Mrs. Stowe can wear a full skirt and a blouse, if she prefers.

President of the United States The performer can wear a suit or a sport jacket and pants, a dress shirt, and a tie.

General Mainwaring The performer can wear a green or tan shirt and a tie. The general should be adorned with medals, which can be made from a variety of materials—ribbon, oaktag, construction paper, metallic paper, and foil. The student can decorate the medals and attach them to the costume with large safety pins. Four stars taped to each shoulder will complete the uniform.

Sergeant The sergeant should be dressed in the same basic costume as General Mainwaring. Instead of wearing the medals and stars, however, he or she should wear a three-striped chevron on each sleeve.

Narrator and Townspeople The rest of the cast can be dressed in school clothes, with the addition of hats, ties, vests, and sweaters to help them feel in character. The student playing the Mayor could wear a bow tie.

PROPS

To give the effect of all the money in the world, the students can stuff several trash bags of different sizes with crumpled newspaper. Suggest that they tie the bags and label them with monetary units from around the world, such as marks, pounds, yen, rubles, lire, francs, pesos, and dollars. Have them place the money bags near Quentin's chair.

Macmillan/McGraw-Hill

WHO·DUN·IT

?

WOO KNOWS

BY ANNE M. MIRANDA

CAST

OFFSTAGE VOICE
MS. WOO
OLIVIA WOO
MANNY THE PARROT
DETECTIVE BILLIE

MS. BYRD
MR. LAMB
MS. HOLSTEIN
MR. COLT
MR. BOXER

SETTING
A travel agency

Wanted
Ms. Holstein

Wanted
Ms. Byrd

Wanted
Mr. Boxer

Wanted
Mr. Lamb

Wanted
Mr. Colt

PROLOGUE

[*The stage is dark.*]

SOUND EFFECTS: [*footsteps; door being unlocked, opened, and shut; footsteps; safe door being unlocked, opened, closed, and locked; footsteps; chair scraping across a floor; jingling of keys; click of a switch; hum of a computer*]

OFFSTAGE VOICE: [*soft whisper*] Now, let's see what we've got here . . .

SOUND EFFECTS: [*clicking of a computer keyboard*]

OFFSTAGE VOICE: [*singing softly*] Baa, baa, black sheep, have you any wool? Yes, sir, yes, sir, three bags full. . . .

ACT I

[*Lights up*]

MS. WOO: Good morning, Olivia! How did you sleep? I made you some toast, and there's orange juice in the fridge.

OLIVIA: Thanks, Mom.

MS. WOO: Well, now that the Memorial Day weekend is over, I've got a busy schedule for the next couple of months.

OLIVIA: I'm glad *I'm* on vacation!

MS. WOO: Lucky you! Summer is a good time to slow down for most people, but not travel agents. We're still busy planning other people's vacations. Speaking of plans, what are you doing today?

OLIVIA: I really don't know, Mom. My detective business seems to be pretty slow these days—I wonder if it has anything to do with the hot weather we've been having. It's been a while since I've had any detecting to do.

MS. WOO: So I've noticed.

OLIVIA: If it would be all right with you, maybe I'll spend the day at your office. I could help you out on the computer.

MS. WOO: That would be great, Olivia.

SOUND EFFECTS: [*thud of newspaper against the door*]

MS. WOO: That must be the newspaper.

OLIVIA: Don't get up, Mom. I'll get it.

SOUND EFFECTS: [*door opening and closing, rustling of paper*]

MS. WOO: See anything interesting?

OLIVIA: I'll say! Just listen to this headline: QUADRUPLETS BORN AT MEMORIAL HOSPITAL. How about that? Four babies born on Memorial Day!

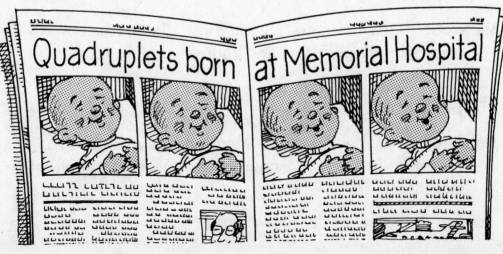

Macmillan/McGraw-Hill

MS. WOO: There must have been quite a bit of excitement at the hospital on *that* day! Anything else?

OLIVIA: Just the usual. . . . No, wait! You won't believe this! "MEMORIAL DAY BREAK-INS. Five homes in the area were burglarized over the Memorial Day weekend. According to the police, in each case the owners were on vacation. The homeowners were contacted and have given permission for their names to be released. The burglary victims are: James and Carol Janson, 35 Maple Street; Victoria Temple, 249 Oak Street; Lisa and Jeff Campo, 19 Washington Avenue; Buzz Saw, 119 West Main Street; Keesha and Ben Owens, 310 Lincoln Drive."

MS. WOO: Hmmm . . . Those names certainly sound familiar. Let me see that paper a minute, will you?

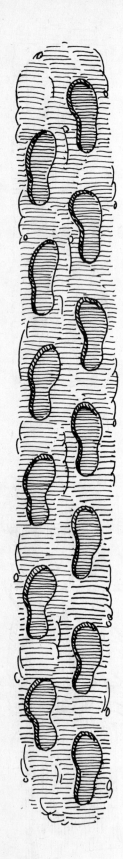

OLIVIA: Are any of them your clients?

MS. WOO: I think almost all of them are—everyone except Buzz Saw, that is. I've never heard of him.

OLIVIA: Mom, don't you remember? Buzz Saw is that rock star I told you about—the one who just moved into town. His real name is Bob Jones.

MS. WOO: Bob Jones? Now let me think. . . . Of course! I remember now. His secretary called me last week and had me book airline tickets for him using his real name. He must like to travel incognito. I just never made the connection.

OLIVIA: That means that *all* these people are your clients.

MS. WOO: You're right. What a coincidence!

OLIVIA: I'd say it's more than just a coincidence, Mom—it's downright suspicious. We'd better go over to the office and check your files right away.

MS. WOO: I hate to say it, Olivia, but this may turn out to be that mystery you were hoping for. Let's get moving.

SOUND EFFECTS: [*traffic sounds, footsteps*]

OLIVIA: Well, Mom, the office door hasn't been forced, and there are no broken windows.

SOUND EFFECTS: [*key turning in lock, door opening and closing*]

MANNY: Squawk. Good morning, good morning. Can I help you?

OLIVIA: I wish you could, Manny! Yes, sir, do I ever!

MANNY: Squawk! Baa, baa, black sheep, have you any wool? Yes, sir! Yes, sir! Three bags full. Squawk!

OLIVIA: Hey, Manny, you've learned a new song. I've never heard you sing *that* one before. I wonder who taught it to you.

MS. WOO: Well, this is reassuring. Everything seems to be just as I left it on Friday.

OLIVIA: What about your disks? Are there any missing?

MS. WOO: I keep the disks in the safe with the tickets. Here's the key to the safe. Go ahead and check.

OLIVIA: Okay, I've got it open. What disks am I looking for?

MS. WOO: Look for the one with last week's dates on the label.

OLIVIA: Here it is—May 25th to May 31st. Safe and sound. Let's check the names against the list in the paper.

MS. WOO: Okay, just let me unlock the computer and we'll see.

SOUND EFFECTS: [*chair scraping across a floor, jingling of keys, click of a switch, hum of a computer, clicking of a computer keyboard*]

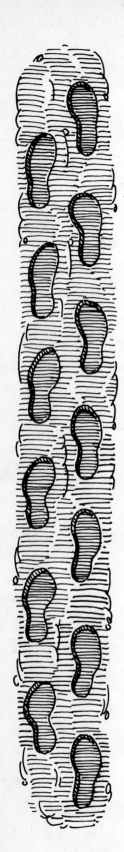

MS. WOO: Hmmm . . . Well, there's no doubt about it. All the names in the paper are on this disk. They're my clients, all right. Those people all left on their vacations last week, and I made their travel plans.

OLIVIA: Did you book them on the same airline by any chance?

MS. WOO: Unfortunately not. They all had different destinations, flew on different airlines, and left on different days. I'm afraid there's absolutely no connection there.

OLIVIA: Then the only way the Memorial Day Burglar could have gotten all those names was from *your* files.

MS. WOO: It certainly looks that way. I'm calling the police this minute.

SOUND EFFECTS: [*dialing telephone*]

MS. WOO: Hello? May I speak with Detective Billie, please? This is Ms. Woo of the Paradise Travel Agency. . . . What? He's on his way here now? I see. Thank you.

OLIVIA: Mom, surely Detective Billie doesn't suspect you!

MS. WOO: Well, he may not suspect me. But by talking to each of the burglary victims, he has probably figured out that I do have the information about everyone's vacation.

OLIVIA: But there must be a way someone else could have gotten access to this information.

MS. WOO: There's only one way that I can think of.

OLIVIA: And that's by copying that disk!

MS. WOO: The trouble is, I don't see how. To keep something like this from happening, I always store the disks in the safe, and I always lock my computer when I leave the office. I'm the only one who has those two keys.

OLIVIA: Right, and don't forget, when we arrived this morning, the door to the office was locked as usual.

SOUND EFFECTS: [*knock at the door, door opening and closing*]

DETECTIVE BILLIE: Good morning, Ms. Woo. Hi, Olivia. I heard on my car radio that you had called the station, so I guess you've probably figured out why I'm here. I must say it's a big help to have "Whodunit" Woo right on the scene.

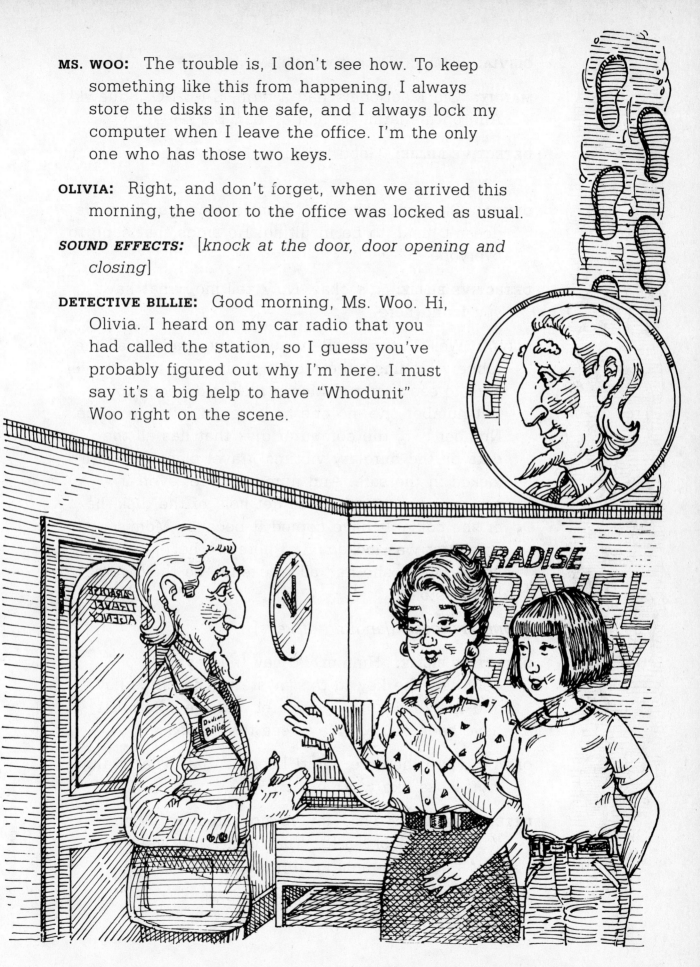

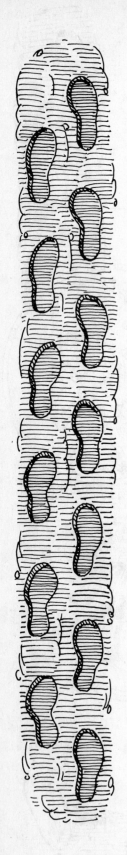

OLIVIA: Thanks, Detective Billie.

MANNY: Old MacDonald had a farm, E-I-E-I-O. Squawk! And on his farm, he had a goat, E-I-E-I-O!

DETECTIVE BILLIE: Good morning, Manny. And thanks a lot!

OLIVIA: Oh, I apologize for Manny, Detective Billie. He doesn't mean to be insulting. He sings that song to everyone.

DETECTIVE BILLIE: It's okay. Now, tell me, what have you found here?

OLIVIA: Well, Detective Billie, when we realized all the robbery victims were Mom's clients, we rushed over here to see if any of Mom's files had been stolen. But number one, no one had broken into the office. Number two, the computer disk that has all the data on the burglary victims' travel plans was still locked in the safe. And number three, even if someone had managed to get hold of the disk, he or she couldn't have copied it because Mom's computer was locked. And here are her keys—which she had all weekend—so they weren't lost or stolen.

SOUND EFFECTS: [*jangling of keys*]

DETECTIVE BILLIE: Hmmm. I'd say the keys are definitely the key to *this* mystery. The office key and the keys to the computer and the safe must have been copied. May I see them, please?

OLIVIA: Here they are. Wait! Look at that! That orange stuff looks like wax!

DETECTIVE BILLIE: That, my young detective, is just what we're looking for. That wax is the very kind that's used for making impressions of keys.

OLIVIA: Now we're getting somewhere!

SOUND EFFECTS: [*telephone ringing*]

MS. WOO: Paradise Travel Agency. May I help you? Yes . . . yes, he's here. It's for you, Detective.

DETECTIVE BILLIE: Billie here. What's up? Uh-huh. Okay, I'll be there in fifteen minutes.

SOUND EFFECTS: [*telephone receiver being replaced*]

DETECTIVE BILLIE: I'm sorry; something urgent has just come up. I've got to go, but I'll be back later so we can continue our discussion.

MS. WOO: All right. We'll be here.

SOUND EFFECTS: [*door opening and closing*]

OLIVIA: Mom, I don't think Detective Billie suspects you of being involved, but I'd like to figure this out. Let's start with the keys. The burglaries didn't occur until the weekend, even though some of your clients left on vacation several days before that. That means the burglar probably didn't have the keys until Friday. So the burglar was probably *here* on Friday, and . . .

MS. WOO: And what?

OLIVIA: And since you *never* leave your keys lying around, you probably gave the burglar the keys for some seemingly innocent reason. Let's start with who was here Friday.

Macmillan/McGraw-Hill

MS. WOO: Here's my appointment book. Let's see, at 10:15, Ms. Holstein came in to plan her vacation. At noon, Mr. Boxer came to pick up my car for repairs. At 1:30, Mr. Colt came in to talk about his vacation. At 2:30, Mr. Lamb came in to pick up some travel brochures. And at 5:30, Ms. Byrd came in to clean the office.

OLIVIA: So there were five people in the office on Friday. Do you remember if anyone borrowed your keys?

MS. WOO: Well, Ms. Byrd always uses the keys to open the supply closet when she comes in to clean.

OLIVIA: That's one.

MS. WOO: Now, Olivia, you know that Ms. Byrd is as honest as the day is long.

OLIVIA: I agree, but I'm sure the police will say that *anyone* who had access to those keys is a suspect. How about the others?

MS. WOO: Well, Mr. Boxer from the garage came to check the rattle I noticed in the engine. He took the keys so that he could take the car for a test drive around the block.

OLIVIA: That's two.

MS. WOO: Hmmm . . . Ms. Holstein used the lavatory key while she was here—and Mr. Lamb used the lavatory key, too!

OLIVIA: That's four! Everyone had the keys except Mr. Colt.

MS. WOO: Wait a minute! Mr. Boxer had to rush off for some unexplained reason. So when he saw Mr. Colt coming in, he gave Mr. Colt the keys to return to me.

OLIVIA: That's five out of five! Everyone who was in here on Friday had your keys at one time or another.

MS. WOO: Olivia, some of those people are coming in again today.

OLIVIA: What luck! Maybe we can do some detective work on our own before Detective Billie gets back.

MS. WOO: Just what do you have in mind?

OLIVIA: Well, one thing we know is that the Memorial Day Burglar knows how to operate your computer. If we can find out who among those five people knows how to run a computer like yours, that would be a big clue.

MS. WOO: That's a great idea, but how will we find out?

OLIVIA: I'm a kid. They'll never be suspicious of *me*. I'll get them talking about computers and act as if I don't know much about them. I think they'll swallow it.

MANNY: There was an old lady, who swallowed a fly. I don't know why she swallowed a fly!

OLIVIA: Too bad Manny can't tell us. I'll bet he knows.

Act II

SOUND EFFECTS: [*knock on the door, door opening and closing, footsteps*]

OLIVIA: Hello, Ms. Byrd. You look chipper this morning!

MANNY: Old MacDonald had a farm, E-I-E-I-O. Squawk! And on his farm, he had a chicken, E-I-E-I-O!

MS. BYRD: That Manny! He's the smartest parrot! He and I talk all the time. Sometimes I even teach him a song.

OLIVIA: Oh, really? He's just learned a new tune. You didn't happen to teach him "Baa, Baa, Black Sheep," by any chance?

MS. BYRD: No, but I once taught him how to sing "Kookaburra." He learned it in no time. Well, I came by to get my pay.

MS. WOO: Of course, Ms. Byrd. Why don't you take a seat while I write out a check.

MS. BYRD: Thanks. I'll perch right here.

OLIVIA: When you were here on Friday afternoon, did you find a game disk lying around?

MS. BYRD: What's a game disk?

OLIVIA: A computer disk. You know, a little, square, black, plastic thing with a hole in the middle.

MS. BYRD: Your mother never leaves anything out. Why don't you look in that box on the desk. I think that's where she keeps those things when she's working at her computer.

SOUND EFFECTS: [*door opening and closing*]

MS. WOO: Good morning, Mr. Lamb.

MANNY: Old MacDonald had a farm, E-I-E-I-O. Squawk! And on his farm, he had a sheep, E-I-E-I-O!

MS. WOO: That's enough, Manny. I didn't expect to see you today, Mr. Lamb. Did you decide to go to Sheepshead Bay?

MR. LAMB: Actually, I've changed my mind. I've decided to take that around-the-world cruise I've always dreamed of. This would be a good time for me to go. Do you think you can arrange it? I'd like to leave as soon as possible.

MS. WOO: An around-the-world cruise? Lucky you, Mr. Lamb! We can begin planning it just as soon as I finish with Ms. Byrd.

MS. BYRD: Oh, I'm in no hurry. Go ahead and help Mr. Lamb. I'll just feed Manny and change his water while I'm waiting.

MS. WOO: Thank you, Ms. Byrd. . . . Oh, dear, the reservations computer is down. There's a message saying that full service should be restored in a few minutes. Mr. Lamb, I'm afraid we'll just have to wait for a bit.

SOUND EFFECTS: [*door opening and closing*]

OLIVIA: Good morning, Ms. Holstein. Nice day, isn't it?

MANNY: Old MacDonald had a farm, E-I-E-I-O. Squawk! And on his farm, he had a cow, E-I-E-I-O!

MS. HOLSTEIN: Who taught that bird to sing that utterly ridiculous song?

OLIVIA: I'm sorry, Ms. Holstein. How may we help you?

MS. HOLSTEIN: I just dropped in to pick up my tickets. I'm leaving for my vacation tomorrow. I'm so excited.

MR. LAMB: Ah, Bermuda—pink sand and sunny skies!

MS. BYRD: Oh, yes, I hear Bermuda is beautiful this time of year.

OLIVIA: Wow! Ms. Holstein, excuse me for interrupting, but does that new red sports car out in front belong to you?

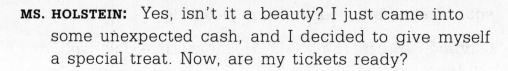

MS. HOLSTEIN: Yes, isn't it a beauty? I just came into some unexpected cash, and I decided to give myself a special treat. Now, are my tickets ready?

MS. WOO: Your tickets are ready, but I'd like to double-check your seat assignment. Could you wait just a few minutes? The reservations computer is temporarily down.

MS. HOLSTEIN: The computer is down? What does that mean?

MR. LAMB: Ms. Woo gets information about reservations from a central computer, and sometimes things go wrong with the equipment. It's usually just a short wait until they clear up the problem.

OLIVIA: I know I've seen you using a computer at the library, Ms. Holstein. Isn't it like my mother's?

MS. HOLSTEIN: Oh, no, we have different computers, and we use different software. I must confess I'm just becoming computer literate—the library system is the only one I know.

> **MR. COLT:** Knock, knock, anybody here? Howdy, y'all!

> **MS. WOO:** Hello, Mr. Colt. Pull up a chair.

> **MANNY:** Old MacDonald had a farm, E-I-E-I-O. Squawk! And on his farm, he had a horse, E-I-E-I-O!

> **MR. COLT:** I wish Manny knew a nice Western song like "Home, Home on the Range." I'd teach it to him myself, but I can't carry a tune in a bucket. Well, enough about music. I'm here to pick up some tickets.

MS. HOLSTEIN: Oh, are you going on vacation, too?

MR. COLT: Yup, and I can't wait! Sagebrush!
Tumbleweeds! Wide open spaces!

MR. LAMB: Ah, yes, Texas, the Lone Star State. Have
you . . .

MR. BOXER: Excuse me, the door was open. Hello, all.
Hi, Manny.

MANNY: Old MacDonald had a farm, E-I-E-I-O. Squawk!
And on his farm, he had a dog, E-I-E-I-O!

MS. WOO: Mr. Boxer! I have a bone to pick with you.
You didn't fix my car on Friday.

MR. BOXER: I knew I'd be in the doghouse. You see,
Ms. Woo, your car didn't have a serious problem,
and I was really worried about my wife. So I rushed
home. Just in time, too. I took her right to the
hospital.

MS. WOO: Goodness! Was she hurt? Is it serious?

MR. BOXER: No, no, everything is great! My wife had quadruplets on Memorial Day! Two girls and two boys—everybody's doing just fine, thank you.

OLIVIA: Oh, wow! We read the headline in the paper just this morning, but we didn't realize it was about *you*.

MS. WOO: And your wife, too, of course!

ALL: Congratulations!

MS. BYRD: Raising four children can be pretty expensive.

MR. BOXER: True, but we'll manage. Say, what's that flickering?

MS. WOO: Oh, the fluorescent light bulb is about to go out. I'll just go downstairs and get the ladder and a new bulb.

SOUND EFFECTS: [*footsteps, door opening*]

MR. COLT: If that's my disk in the machine, I can check to see if my flight has been booked.

MR. LAMB: First, you'll have to bring up your file. Ms. Woo was working on mine.

OLIVIA: You may have to wait, Mr. Colt. The central reservations computer is down. Of course, it may be fixed by now, but I don't know how to find out.

MR. COLT: Let me try. They don't call me "Hacker" for nothing.

MR. BOXER: Maybe I can help you. We use the same computer down at the garage.

MS. WOO: I'm back. Sorry I took so long, but I had to find a screwdriver. What's everyone doing at my computer?

OLIVIA: It's okay, Mom. We're just trying to find out if the central computer has come back up again.

MS. WOO: I'll take care of it. But first I have to fix that flickering light. It will only take me a minute.

MR. LAMB: Can I help, Ms. Woo? I'm real handy—there's nothing mechanical or electrical that I can't fix. I'll have that bulb changed in two shakes of a lamb's tail!

MS. WOO: Thanks, Mr. Lamb. I'll just get back to that computer.

SOUND EFFECTS: [*clanking of tools*]

MR. LAMB: [*singing softly*] Baa, baa, black sheep, have you any wool?

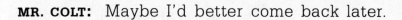

MR. COLT: Maybe I'd better come back later.

MR. BOXER: Do you need a lift? I'm going downtown.

MR. LAMB: [*singing softly*] Yes, sir, yes, sir, three bags full.

MS. WOO: I'm sorry to keep you waiting so long, Ms. Byrd.

MR. LAMB: [*singing softly*] One for my master, one for my dame.

MS. BYRD: No problem, Ms. Woo. I'm enjoying myself.

SOUND EFFECTS: [*door opening and closing*]

DETECTIVE BILLIE: I'm back, Ms. Woo. Ahem! May I have your attention please! This office is being investigated in connection with the Memorial Day burglaries. I'll have to ask everyone to leave now.

MS. BYRD AND MR. LAMB: Under investigation?

MR. COLT AND MS. HOLSTEIN: Burglaries?

MR. BOXER: Good grief!

OLIVIA: Excuse me, Detective Billie. The Memorial Day Burglar is in this room right now. I'm sure of it.

MS. HOLSTEIN: It's best to leave police work to the police, young lady.

DETECTIVE BILLIE: I'll handle this, ma'am. That's a serious accusation, Olivia. What evidence do you have?

OLIVIA: The Memorial Day Burglar copied my mother's client files from her disk. That's how the thief found out which houses would be empty over the weekend, right?

DETECTIVE BILLIE: That sounds plausible. Go on.

OLIVIA: As you said, it's a question of keys. Ms. Byrd uses Mom's keys every week when she cleans the office. She could easily have made wax impressions of them. But Ms. Byrd has worked for my mother for a long time and has never taken so much as a paper clip. Besides, Ms. Byrd knows absolutely nothing about computers.

MS. BYRD: She's right. I don't know a thing about computers.

OLIVIA: Ms. Holstein has just come into a lot of money. See her expensive new car outside? Also, she borrowed the keys on Friday to use the lavatory. She does use a computer at the library, *but* she doesn't know anything about my mother's software program. The thief would have to know about that program to get the computer to run and to copy the disk.

MS. HOLSTEIN: That's right. I don't know anything about her mother's computer.

OLIVIA: Which brings us to Mr. Boxer. Mr. Boxer took the keys on Friday to give Mom's car a test drive around the block. He also knows a lot about computers. In fact, he has an identical machine at the garage. Also, as Ms. Byrd pointed out, Mr. Boxer certainly needs money just now.

MR. BOXER: But I was at the hospital from Friday afternoon through Tuesday night.

OLIVIA: Yes, I think all of us would agree that Mr. Boxer has an unshakable alibi for the Memorial Day weekend.

DETECTIVE BILLIE: All right, who's next?

OLIVIA: Well, Mr. Boxer asked Mr. Colt to return my mom's keys to her, so Mr. Colt could have made an impression of them. What's more, his nickname is "Hacker." A hacker is someone who can do almost anything with a computer.

DETECTIVE BILLIE: Then he could have gotten the names of all those people who were robbed.

OLIVIA: Right.

DETECTIVE BILLIE: Sounds suspicious to me!

OLIVIA: I'm not so sure that Mr. Colt is your man, though. Don't forget, Mr. Lamb had Mom's keys last Friday when he borrowed them to use the lavatory. He also knows a lot about computers. And when he came in today, he wanted to change his plans from a weekend trip to an around-the-world cruise. That takes a lot of money.

DETECTIVE BILLIE: But that's not real evidence.

OLIVIA: True. But how did he know Ms. Holstein was going to Bermuda? *And* that Mr. Colt was going to Texas?

MR. LAMB: I guessed. I'm good at putting two and two together.

Macmillan/McGraw-Hill

DETECTIVE BILLIE: Well, Olivia, you may not have solved the case, but at least you've narrowed the number of suspects down to two—Mr. Colt and Mr. Lamb. Now if you two gentlemen would kindly accompany me to the station for further questioning . . .

OLIVIA: I don't think that will be necessary, Detective Billie. You see, the thief has to be able to sing.

DETECTIVE BILLIE: Excuse me? What does singing have to do with it?

OLIVIA: When Mom and I arrived at the office this morning, Manny was singing a song that we had never heard him sing before. Mom was here until late on Friday. That means Manny must have learned that song between Friday night and Monday night—*a period when the office was closed*.

DETECTIVE BILLIE: I follow you.

OLIVIA: Just now, Mr. Lamb sang the *very same song* while he was changing the light bulb. My theory is that Mr. Lamb is in the habit of humming or singing while he works. I think he was singing "Baa, Baa, Black Sheep" when he was here copying Mom's files.

MR. LAMB: More guesswork. Ridiculous!

OLIVIA: And, finally, Mr. Lamb is very handy. He said so himself. If you search his workshop, I'm sure you'll find the wax he used to make the impressions of Mom's keys plus a machine that makes duplicate keys.

MR. LAMB: Drat that junior detective and her feathered friend!

DETECTIVE BILLIE: Okay, let's go quietly, Mr. Lamb. Thanks, "Whodunit" Woo, you've done it again!

MS. WOO: Olivia, you're terrific!

OLIVIA: Thanks, Mom. Mr. Lamb turned out to be a real wolf in sheep's clothing. Oh, and let's not forget to thank Manny. Without him, I never would have cracked this case.

MANNY: Baa, baa, black sheep, have you any wool?
Yes, sir, yes, sir, three bags full.
One for my master, one for my dame,
And one for the naughty crook
Who won't steal again! Squawk! Squawk!

BLOCKING DIAGRAM

Arrange nine chairs or stools, as shown. The narrator can use a music stand to hold the script. The cast member playing the part of Mr. Lamb should record the Off-Stage Voice lines in a slightly disguised voice as part of the sound-effects tape.

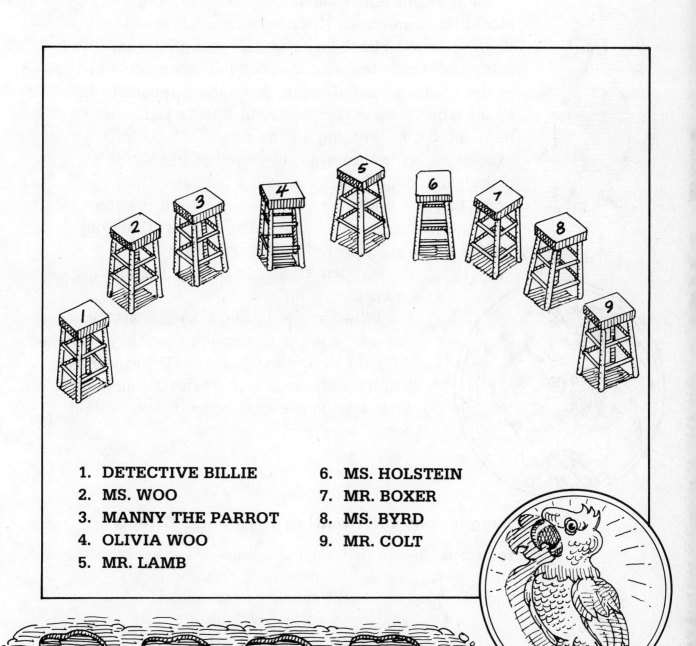

1. **DETECTIVE BILLIE**
2. **MS. WOO**
3. **MANNY THE PARROT**
4. **OLIVIA WOO**
5. **MR. LAMB**
6. **MS. HOLSTEIN**
7. **MR. BOXER**
8. **MS. BYRD**
9. **MR. COLT**

SOUND EFFECTS

Creating sound effects is a process of trial and error. Students should be encouraged to try alternative methods for producing realistic sounds and to experiment with different durations of a given sound effect.

Each sound effect should be tested by tape recording it and then listening to the playback. Will the sound effect be convincing to a listening audience? Once the sound effect has been produced to the students' satisfaction, have them record it on audio tape. Then a master sound-effects tape can be created by including all the sound effects in exactly the same order as they appear in the script. If the same sound effect is called for more than once, suggest to students that they record it each time it appears in the script. Also suggest that they let the tape run silently for about five seconds between recorded effects to allow time to start and stop the recorder.

When students begin to rehearse in earnest, it is recommended that they rehearse with the sound-effects tape. Using the tape will help students anticipate the amount of "wait time" needed to allow for the sound effect.

Suggestions for Creating the Sound Effects

footsteps Record the sound of actual footsteps (approaching or receding, depending on the context), possibly using a different person for each character. The "walkers" should wear shoes with leather soles and walk on a bare floor. Ms. Woo can wear heels to differentiate her steps from Olivia's. Decide at what pace each person should walk.

Macmillan/McGraw-Hill

door being unlocked Jangle a set of keys and then unlock a door.

door opening and closing Record an actual door opening and closing. Try several doors to see which one sounds best.

safe being unlocked, opened, closed, and locked First record the sound of a key in a lock. Then open a metal door, such as the door of a metal cabinet; pause; close the door; and lock it.

chair scraping across floor Pull a chair across an uncarpeted floor.

jingling of keys Jingle several keys on a ring.

sound of a switch Record the click of a computer, light, or TV switch.

hum of a computer Use the real thing, or record the sound of a hair dryer from a distance.

clicking of a computer keyboard Type on a computer or on a quiet electric typewriter.

thud of newspaper Roll a newspaper, and rap it once against a table.

rustling of paper Rub two sheets of paper together near the microphone.

traffic sounds Record the sound of traffic at a busy intersection.

dialing telephone Lift a telephone receiver. Dial a seven-digit number (or enter one on a touch-tone phone). Keep the switch depressed during the dialing so you don't actually make a call.

knock at door Knock on a wooden table, a door, or a board.

telephone ringing Record the real thing. Pick up after three rings.

telephone being hung up Hold the microphone close to a telephone as you hang up the receiver.

clanking of tools Put silverware or other metal items in a box, and rummage through them.

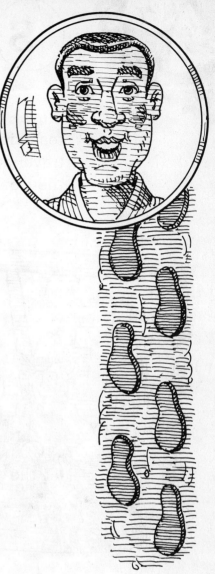

SET DECORATION

Travel posters for Ms. Woo's office will add a realistic and decorative touch. Actual posters from a travel agency can be used, or students can create their own posters on oaktag or poster board.

Macmillan/McGraw-Hill

NAT LOVE
WESTERN HERO

BY
JUDITH BAUER STAMPER

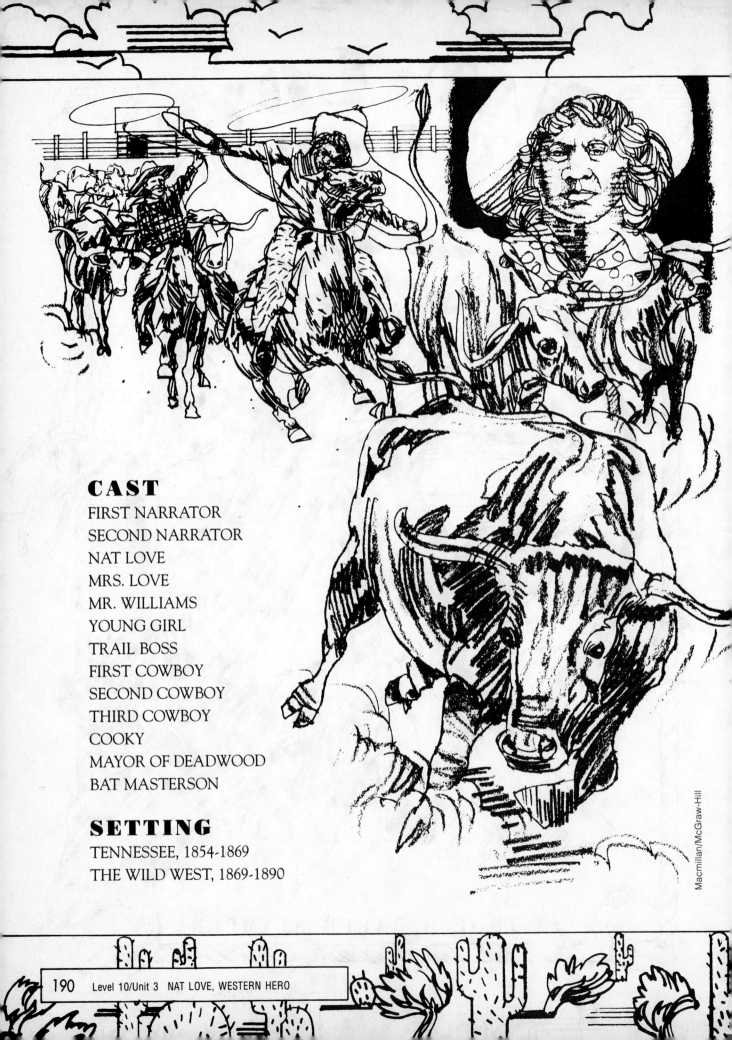

CAST

FIRST NARRATOR
SECOND NARRATOR
NAT LOVE
MRS. LOVE
MR. WILLIAMS
YOUNG GIRL
TRAIL BOSS
FIRST COWBOY
SECOND COWBOY
THIRD COWBOY
COOKY
MAYOR OF DEADWOOD
BAT MASTERSON

SETTING

TENNESSEE, 1854-1869
THE WILD WEST, 1869-1890

Macmillan/McGraw-Hill

FIRST NARRATOR: Back in the days of the Wild West, there was one cowboy who could outride, outrope, and outshoot all the rest. He was an African American whose name was Nat Love, but everyone called him by his nickname, Deadwood Dick.

SECOND NARRATOR: Nat spent most of his life on the range—gentling wild horses, branding cattle, and herding steers across hundreds of miles of open prairie. Near the end of his life, Nat recorded all his adventures in an autobiography titled *The Life and Adventures of Nat Love, Better Known in the Cattle Country as "Deadwood Dick."* Many of the exciting adventures in its pages read like tall tales right out of the Wild West.

NAT: I was born a slave in an old log cabin in Tennessee in 1854. I never knew the exact day of my birth because in those days, no one thought to keep track of slave babies' birthdays. My pa worked on a plantation owned by a white man named Robert Love, and my ma was in charge of the kitchen in the big house.

FIRST NARRATOR: When Nat turned eleven, his life suddenly changed. The Civil War was over, and Nat was now free. But freedom didn't make Nat's life much easier. His father died, and the Love family was poor and hungry. Nat knew that his family's survival depended on him.

NAT: There's no food left in the cupboard, Ma, and all the money you and Pa managed to save is gone. Someone has got to feed us, and I reckon that means me.

MRS. LOVE: How will we ever get along without your pa? You're too young and too small to go out and work like a man.

NAT: I may be young, but I'm free. I'll use my freedom to go out and get a job. I was talking with Mr. Brooks today. He promised he would give me a job working on his farm. He's offering to pay me $1.50 a month—that's not a fortune, but something is better than nothing. I'm starting work tomorrow.

MRS. LOVE: Your pa would be proud of you. Someday, you're going to grow up and make something of yourself. I just know it.

NAT: That's exactly what I aim to do, Ma.

SECOND NARRATOR: The very next day, Nat started his job and soon began bringing home potatoes, bacon, cornmeal, and molasses. He worked hard six days out of seven, and he always shared what he made with his mother and the other children in the family.

FIRST NARRATOR: Then one Sunday—his day off—he found another job. This job was the start of his life as a cowboy. It all happened at a nearby horse ranch owned by Mr. Williams.

Macmillan/McGraw-Hill

MR. WILLIAMS: Hey, Nat! Come on over here. I want to talk with you for a minute.

NAT: Sure thing, Mr. Williams.

MR. WILLIAMS: Looky here, Nat. I've got a bunch of wild horses that need gentling. Word has it that you're good with horses. Folks also say that there's not much that scares you.

NAT: Well, sir, horses don't scare me—wild or tamed. And I wouldn't mind making a little extra money.

MR. WILLIAMS: Tell you what. I'll give you ten cents for every wild horse you can gentle for me. How does that sound?

NAT: That sounds just fine to me. You've got yourself a deal! Just lead me to the horse.

SECOND NARRATOR: Nat mounted one of Mr. Williams's wild horses and stuck to it like a leech. No matter how much the horse kicked and bucked, Nat clung to its back. Mr. Williams and Nat were both happy with the deal they had made. From then on, Nat spent Sundays breaking in horses and earning ten cents for each horse he gentled.

FIRST NARRATOR: Then, one day, Mr. Williams talked to Nat about the wildest horse in his stable—a horse named Black Highwayman. Nobody had ever been able to stay on Black Highwayman's back long enough to ride him.

MR. WILLIAMS: You've gentled a lot of horses for me in the past few months. But I've got one that's meaner and smarter than all the rest of 'em put together. For some reason, he just won't take to the feeling of a human on his back. Do you think you're ready to try to gentle Black Highwayman?

NAT: Sir, that horse has one mighty mean temper, and you and I both know it. I might be willing to try to gentle him, but I'm not willing to do it for ten cents.

MR. WILLIAMS: Well, just what amount of money do you have in mind?

NAT: I was thinking about fifty cents. You know, I'm taking quite a risk getting on a mean horse like that.

MR. WILLIAMS: It's a risk, all right, but fifty cents is too much. Would you be willing to do it for fifteen?

NAT: I value my life too much to throw it away for fifteen cents, Mr. Williams. How about twenty-five cents paid in advance?

MR. WILLIAMS: It's a deal. Here's your money, and good luck.

YOUNG GIRL: Hey, Nat! Don't try to ride that horse. You'll get yourself killed for sure!

NAT: It's too late now! I just took the money, and I'm going to gentle that horse if it's the last thing I do. Just stand back and watch me.

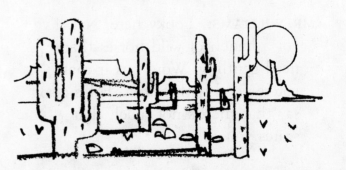

YOUNG GIRL: Will you look at that! He's doing it. Nat's climbing up on Black Highwayman's back!

FIRST NARRATOR: The second that Nat got on its back, Black Highwayman took off like a shot across the countryside. Nat knew he would either break the horse or break his neck.

YOUNG GIRL: Hang on, Nat!

FIRST NARRATOR: He hung on for dear life until, finally, the horse wore itself out. With a big grin on his face, Nat brought the horse back to Mr. Williams's stable.

YOUNG GIRL: Hooray! You did it! You really earned that twenty-five cents.

FIRST NARRATOR: But when Nat reached into his pocket to find his hard-earned money, it was gone. He had lost it on his wild ride!

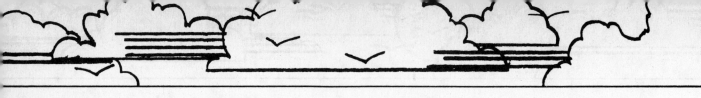

SECOND NARRATOR: Nat remained home with his family until he turned fifteen. About that time, he got the urge to go out and see the world. He felt confident that he could take care of himself, so he said good-bye to his mother and headed out West. His destination was Dodge City, Kansas. Located at the end of the Western Cattle Trail, Dodge City had the reputation of being one of the roughest and toughest towns on the frontier. There Nat met up with the trail boss and several cowboys from a big cattle spread in Texas.

TRAIL BOSS: So, tenderfoot, I can tell you're new to these parts. Where are you from?

NAT: I was born and raised in the state of Tennessee, but ever since I can remember, I've always wanted to come out West to be a cowboy. It sounds like the kind of life for me.

FIRST COWBOY: Tennessee, you say? Then you don't know a doggone thing about cattle raising or wild horses.

NAT: Is that so? Well, sir, I'll have you know that I've ridden a few wild horses in my time.

SECOND COWBOY: Why sure, son. You've ridden Tennessee horses—not *real* horses like we have out here. Horses in the West are different—they're wilder and meaner, just like us cowpokes.

NAT: That may be so, but I've never met a horse I couldn't ride.

TRAIL BOSS: I'll tell you what, Nat. I've got a horse called Old Good Eye over in that corral. Now if you stick on that horse, you've got yourself a guaranteed job as a trail hand with my outfit. Is it a deal?

NAT: You bet it's a deal. Here's my handshake on it. I'll saddle up that pony right now and take him for a little ride.

THIRD COWBOY: This should be fun to watch. That tenderfoot doesn't know what he's in for.

FIRST COWBOY: He thinks he can be a cowboy just by coming out West. Old Good Eye will teach Nat Love a lesson that he won't soon forget!

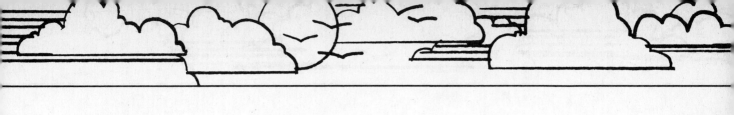

FIRST NARRATOR: But before Nat got on the horse, another black cowboy by the name of Bronco Jim came over and gave Nat a few pointers about riding Old Good Eye. Nat thanked him kindly and then swung one leg over the horse's back. Old Good Eye started to buck like he was being stung by a swarm of hornets.

TRAIL BOSS: By golly! Look at that horse go!

FIRST COWBOY: Young Nat is bouncing mighty high in that saddle!

SECOND COWBOY: He's bouncing, all right, but he's staying on.

SECOND NARRATOR: Nat stuck on until that horse grew too tired to buck anymore. But later, he admitted that it was the worst ride of his entire life.

NAT: That horse rattled every bone in my body and then some!

TRAIL BOSS: You did all right, Nat. And you earned yourself a place in this outfit.

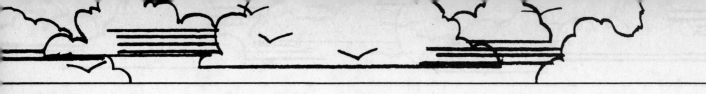

FIRST NARRATOR: The trail boss offered Nat a job that paid thirty dollars a month, and Nat took him up on his offer immediately. He left Dodge City with the outfit and rode with them to their ranch in the panhandle section of Texas.

SECOND NARRATOR: Before long, Nat became one of the best cowhands in the West. He loved the wild and free life on the range. He was good at roping and riding, and soon he became an expert at recognizing the hundreds of different brands used by the ranches to identify their livestock.

TRAIL BOSS: Nat, I hear from the rest of the boys that you've got a good eye for reading brands.

NAT: Shucks, it's not that hard. Why, I can spot a "Double L" or a "Lazy Z" mark from a mile away.

TRAIL BOSS: Well, I'd like to put you in charge of reading brands for this outfit. It will mean more work, but it will also mean a raise in pay.

Macmillan/McGraw-Hill

FIRST NARRATOR: So Nat worked with cowboys from other ranches during the roundups. Cattle from various ranches grazed together on the range, but a few times each year, they would be herded to a central place. There, cowhands from the different ranches would work together to sort them by brand, mark any new calves that had not yet been branded, and count to see how many head of cattle each ranch had.

SECOND NARRATOR: Without this kind of cooperation, the job would never have gotten done. Nat soon became well known among the cowboys for his fair play, and his skill at reading brands was recognized by everyone.

NAT: Now that the cattle are all branded, when is the next big cattle drive?

TRAIL BOSS: Next week we have to drive nearly a thousand head of cattle over the Chisholm Trail. You'll have to be in the saddle pretty much night and day.

FIRST NARRATOR: During the big cattle drives, cowboys rode hundreds of miles. They herded the cattle, leading them across rivers, protecting them, and otherwise making sure they arrived at the end of the trail unharmed. It was exhausting work.

SECOND NARRATOR: After a long day in the saddle, the cowboys gathered around the campfire to share a meal and trade a few stories.

NAT: This is good grub, Cooky. It's just what I need after fifteen hours in the saddle.

COOKY: I put extra hot pepper in it just for you. I know you like your stew hot and spicy!

NAT: *Muchas gracias.* All that chili pepper helps keep me warm inside on these cold nights.

COOKY: Speaking of cold nights, my blanket got soaked when we forded the river this afternoon.

NAT: Here, friend, take mine. I've got your hot pepper stew to keep me warm.

COOKY: Why, thanks. I heard tell you were a real *compadre.* Now I know it's the truth.

FIRST COWBOY: Say, Nat, I heard a story about you last spring. Some cowpunchers up north Wyoming way were talking about how you saved a buddy of theirs during a blizzard.

NAT: Aw, any other cowboy would have done the same. You see, my buddy and I were stuck in this big snowstorm without horses, and he got hurt. I just carried him a bit till we met up with help. If we cowboys don't stick together, none of us will survive.

FIRST NARRATOR: Being a cowboy was a rough life, all right. But nobody was better suited to it than Nat Love. He was good at riding and roping and shooting. But, best of all, he could think straight in a tight situation and find a way out of it.

SECOND NARRATOR: Nat's thinking ability came in real handy one night on the prairie in the Nebraska Territory. Nat was standing watch with a couple of other cowboys after a long day on the trail.

NAT: Look up at that big old moon. It sure puts me in mind of singing a song.

SECOND COWBOY: Maybe you had better not. You might scare the cattle. And we just got 'em all settled down for the night.

NAT: I guess you're right. My singing never was appreciated by man or beast.

THIRD COWBOY: Why don't we all just turn in early? The sky is as clear as can be. There's no chance of a storm spooking the herd. And there are too many of us for cattle rustlers to mess with. What do you say, Nat?

NAT: Sorry, partner, I hate to disagree, but I say we keep watch. You never know what might happen out here on the prairie. We've got over a thousand head of cattle in this herd, and if anything happened to them, I sure wouldn't want to be caught napping by the trail boss.

FIRST COWBOY: Nat's right, but it surely is a peaceful night. How could anything go wrong on a night like this? Well, boys, I'll take the first watch.

FIRST NARRATOR: An hour later, Nat suddenly jumped up out of his bedroll and looked to the north.

NAT: What's that noise in the distance? It sounds a lot like thunder.

FIRST COWBOY: I don't hear a thing. It's only your imagination. Just look at that sky—there's no storm brewing tonight.

THIRD COWBOY: No, Nat's right. There *is* a roaring sound coming from up north. But it's too loud and too steady to be thunder.

NAT: It's buffalo, boys! There's a buffalo stampede heading right for us! We've got to get the cattle out of their way. Rouse all the hands and tell them to saddle up, pronto! We've got to try to drive the cattle out of the path of those buffalo!

SECOND COWBOY: Boys, this sure is going to be some night!

Macmillan/McGraw-Hill

FIRST NARRATOR: It was some night, all right. Nat and the rest of the cowboys did all they could to move the cattle out of the way. They even rode straight into the buffalo stampede, trying to turn the animals aside. After hours of riding and herding and yelling, it was all over.

TRAIL BOSS: Now that the dust has settled, Nat, can you give me some idea of just how bad things are?

NAT: Well, sir, we lost only five head of cattle, but something worse happened. Cal Surcey—that young cowhand who just hired on—got thrown from his horse and was trampled to death by the buffalo.

SECOND NARRATOR: Nat and the other cowhands buried Cal and then, with heavy hearts, they herded the cattle on up the trail to Wyoming.

FIRST NARRATOR: A few years later, in 1876, Nat's outfit got an order to deliver three thousand head of cattle to Deadwood City in the Dakota Territory. It was a long ride, and by the time the cowboys arrived in Deadwood, they were ready to celebrate.

SECOND NARRATOR: Now it just so happened that the next day was Independence Day. And on that day, the town of Deadwood planned to hold a big roping contest for all the cowboys who were in the area. Since it was a holiday, cowpunchers from all over the territory rode into Deadwood City for the competition.

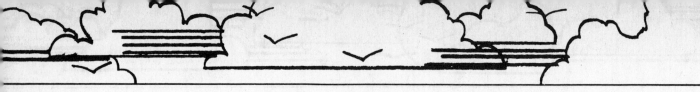

TRAIL BOSS: Hey there, Nat! We're counting on you to enter that roping contest and win it. You're the best cowhand in our outfit. In all my years of cowpunching, I've never seen anybody handle a rope or a horse like you do.

NAT: You'd have to tie me up to keep me out of that contest, boss. I hear they've rounded up the wildest broncos in the territory for us to ride.

TRAIL BOSS: You heard right about that, Nat. But there isn't a horse alive that you can't stick to once you've made up your mind to it.

FIRST NARRATOR: Nat entered the contest, but so did a lot of other cowboys. Each of them had to choose a wild bronco to rope and ride. The cowboy who finished the contest in the fastest time would be the winner. Well, in nine minutes flat, Nat roped, threw, tied, bridled, saddled, and mounted his bronco. Then he rode it until that horse was as tame as a kitten. No other cowboy came even close to his time. The crowd went wild with excitement.

MAYOR: Nat Love, the fair town of Deadwood would like to make you an honorary citizen. You've earned yourself the title of Deadwood Dick, Champion Roper of the West.

NAT: I'm pleased and flattered that you'd give me a nickname in honor of this fine town. Deadwood Dick— that's a handle any cowhand would be proud to carry.

THIRD COWBOY: The day's not over yet, Nat . . . er, I mean, Deadwood Dick. The shooting contest is coming up next. Are you going to win that one, too?

Macmillan/McGraw-Hill

NAT: I aim to give it my best shot. But there's some mighty mean competition ahead. I see my old pal Stormy Jim over there by the corral, and if I'm not mistaken, that's Powder Horn Bill near the hitching post. I hear they never miss anything they aim at.

MAYOR: Come on, Deadwood Dick. Show us how well you can shoot!

SECOND NARRATOR: Well, Nat Love proved that he was the best all-around cowboy in the Dakota Territory. He won both the rifle- and the Colt 45-shooting contests!

MAYOR: Well, I suppose this makes you the official hero of Deadwood City. It is my pleasure to award you the $200 prize money.

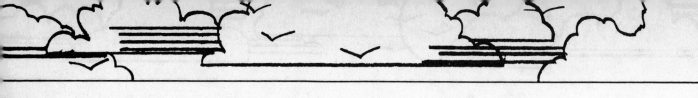

NAT: Thank you kindly, Mayor.

SECOND NARRATOR: From that day on, Nat Love was known throughout cattle country as Deadwood Dick.

FIRST NARRATOR: For fourteen more years, Nat rode the range as a cowboy. His life was filled with one adventure after another. Once he was captured by Indians. They respected the way he had fought, so they nursed his wounds and adopted him into the tribe. After some weeks, though, Nat made a daring escape, riding bareback for a hundred miles to his home in Texas. Another time, Nat almost froze to death during a prairie blizzard, but his luck and his courage pulled him through.

SECOND NARRATOR: By 1890, the old Wild West was fading out of existence and becoming another chapter in the history of America. Nat talked about its passing with his old friend Bat Masterson, the famous sheriff of Dodge City.

NAT: It's real sad what's happening to the West. The buffalo are almost all gone. Houses are being built right smack dab in the middle of the trail where we used to drive herds of cattle up to Dodge City.

BAT MASTERSON: And I hear that the ranches are all fenced in with that newfangled barbed wire, and almost all the cattle are shipped by rail nowadays.

Macmillan/McGraw-Hill

NAT: I surely don't know what the West is coming to, but one thing is certain—they don't need old cowboys like me anymore.

BAT MASTERSON: What are you going to do with yourself if your range-riding days are over?

NAT: I'll tell you one thing I'm *not* going to do. I plumb refuse to sit around here and mope and grow old. I'm thinking about heading over to Denver, Colorado, and hunting down a job there. If the country is going to change, then I'm going to change with it!

BAT MASTERSON: You always were a fighter. Best of luck to you in Denver.

FIRST NARRATOR: Nat moved to Denver, leaving his cowboy life behind him forever. There, he met the woman who was to become Mrs. Nat Love. They got married and settled down in Denver. A short while later, Nat took a job as a Pullman porter on the Denver and Rio Grande Railroad. Soon, he was rolling across the range behind an iron horse instead of riding across it on the back of a real one.

SECOND NARRATOR: As the years passed, Nat often thought back on his days as a cowboy. He decided to write down all the exciting adventures that had come his way as the famous cowboy, Deadwood Dick. Nat summed up what it was like to be a cowboy with these words:

NAT: I, Nat Love, now in my fifty-fourth year, hale, hearty, and happy, will ever cherish a fond and loving feeling for the old days on the range, its exciting adventures, good horses, good and bad men, long venturesome rides, and—last but foremost—the friends I have made and the friends I have gained.

FIRST NARRATOR: And so ends the story of Nat Love, better known in cattle country as Deadwood Dick.

BLOCKING DIAGRAM

Arrange eleven chairs or stools, as shown. The two narrators can use music stands to hold their scripts.

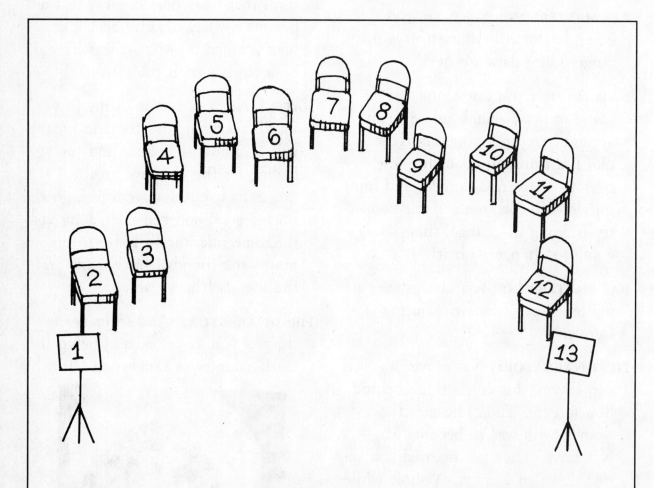

1. FIRST NARRATOR
2. MRS. LOVE
3. YOUNG GIRL
4. MR. WILLIAMS
5. BAT MASTERSON
6. NAT LOVE
7. TRAIL BOSS
8. FIRST COWBOY
9. SECOND COWBOY
10. THIRD COWBOY
11. COOKY
12. MAYOR OF DEADWOOD
13. SECOND NARRATOR

Macmillan/McGraw-Hill

HOME ON THE RANGE

What was the life of a cowboy really like? It was hard! Every spring, vast herds, numbering two or three thousand head, had to be moved from Texas to railroad towns up north so they could be shipped to other parts of the country. And that took skill, organization, and hard work.

A trail boss led a crew of about ten cowboys, a cook, and a wrangler. It was the wrangler's job to take care of the horses. There were seven or eight horses for each cowboy. There had to be fresh horses to ride, plus spare horses in case of accidents. The cook drove the chuck wagon and was in charge of supplies. At times he also served as a barber, a dentist, and even a doctor.

The crew ate breakfast before the sun was up. Then the men broke camp and got the cattle moving in a thin line about a mile or two long. They covered about ten miles each day. A cowboy sat in his saddle all day long, regardless of the weather.

At sundown, the outfit made camp at a spot that the trail boss had scouted out earlier—one that had plenty of water and grass for grazing. Day was done, but the cowboy's work wasn't. Each man was assigned a two-hour watch. Throughout the night, two guards rode in opposite directions around the sleeping cattle, whistling or singing to let them know that a friend was near. At dawn, the routine began again.

Life on the trail was dangerous. The cowboys had to be on constant watch for lightning, stampedes, and attacks.

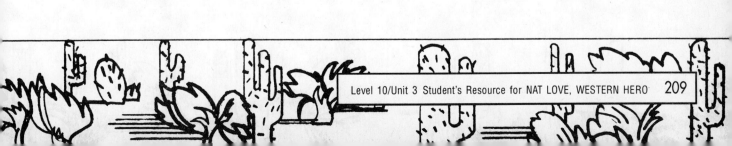

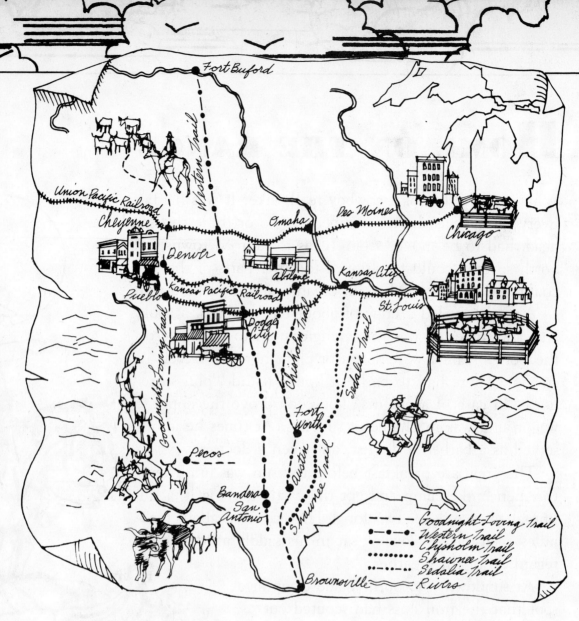

Map legend:

- – – – Goodnight-Loving Trail
- •–•–•– Western Trail
- ••••••• Chisholm Trail
- ••••••• Shawnee Trail
- –••–••– Sedalia Trail
- ~~~~~ Rivers

Map labels: Fort Buford, Union Pacific Railroad, Western Trail, Cheyenne, Omaha, Des Moines, Chicago, Denver, Abilene, Kansas City, St. Louis, Pueblo, Kansas Pacific Railroad, Goodnight-Loving Trail, Dodge City, Chisholm Trail, Sedalia Trail, Pecos, Fort Worth, Austin, Shawnee Trail, Bandera, San Antonio, Brownsville

Even crossing rivers was risky. Fast-flowing water often swept away cattle, horses, and men. The cattle wouldn't swim unless they could see the opposite bank of the river. They wouldn't swim with the sun in their eyes, either. It might take many tries to get a herd across. Cowboys said that the best river crossing was the one that was over.

Days, weeks, and sometimes months went by before cattle and cowboys reached—*town*! It might have been Kansas City, Dodge City, or Abilene in Kansas. Or it could have been Ogallala, Nebraska. After a shave, haircut, bath, some new clothes, and a few days of relaxing, the cowboys hit the trail again—for home.

Macmillan/McGraw-Hill

COSTUME SUGGESTIONS

Narrators The narrators can wear jeans, plaid shirts, and string ties.

Mrs. Love The student playing Nat's mother can be dressed in a long skirt and a blouse, with a large scarf draped around her shoulders. The performer may also wear a neckerchief knotted around her neck.

Nat Love As the play opens, the performer cast as Nat can wear jeans and a plaid shirt with a bandanna. When the narrator explains that Nat decided to go to Dodge City, the student can don a cowboy hat.

Young Girl A long, full skirt with a plain or ruffled blouse would be an appropriate costume for the student playing this part.

Mr. Williams and the Mayor Each of these performers could wear a dark sport jacket, dark pants, a white shirt, and a string tie.

Trail Boss and Cowboys These performers can wear light shirts and jeans, red bandannas tied at the back of the neck, vests, and wide-brimmed hats. They can make a modified version of chaps by cutting long strips from brown paper bags, fringing them with scissors, and taping or safety-pinning the fringes to the outer seam on each pants leg.

Cooky The performer cast as Cooky can wear a white butcher-type apron over a light shirt and jeans.

Bat Masterson This performer can wear dark pants, a dark shirt with a string tie, and a cowboy hat. The performer should also wear a sheriff's badge, which can be made by cutting a star out of oaktag and covering it with foil.

Macmillan/McGraw-Hill

THE NIGHTINGALE

CAST
NARRATOR
TRAVELER 1
TRAVELER 2
GARDENER
NIGHTINGALE
FISHERMAN
FISHERMAN'S WIFE
EMPEROR
EMPRESS
CHAMBERLAIN
COURTIER 1
COURTIER 2
KITCHEN MAID
LADY 1
LADY 2
MESSENGER
JEWELED BIRD
MUSIC MASTER
WATCHMAKER

SETTING
ANCIENT CHINA

BY KATHLEEN M. FISCHER
based on the tale by
Hans Christian Andersen

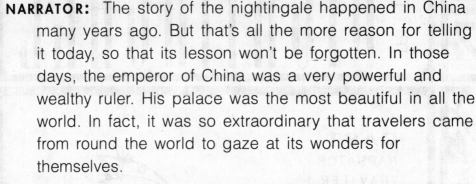

NARRATOR: The story of the nightingale happened in China many years ago. But that's all the more reason for telling it today, so that its lesson won't be forgotten. In those days, the emperor of China was a very powerful and wealthy ruler. His palace was the most beautiful in all the world. In fact, it was so extraordinary that travelers came from round the world to gaze at its wonders for themselves.

TRAVELER 1: Greetings, fellow traveler! I've journeyed to distant lands in search of marvels to write about, yet never have I seen such splendor. Who would believe that a palace could be made of fine porcelain?

TRAVELER 2: Yes, indeed. It's so delicate, so fragile, I must confess I dared touch nothing as I walked through it. I'm a poet, and here in the imperial palace I've found many subjects worthy of my pen.

TRAVELER 1: Perhaps you would care to join me in strolling through the emperor's magnificent gardens.

TRAVELER 2: Nothing would please me more. Ah, look there. The gardener is tying bells to those flowers. How odd!

TRAVELER 1: Most unusual! We must find out why. . . . Forgive us for interrupting your labors, Imperial Gardener. We are visitors to your kingdom and are seeking to understand your customs. Tell us, please, why are you hanging bells on these flowers?

GARDENER: You see, honored travelers, only the rarest and most exquisite flowers are allowed to grow in the emperor's garden. It is my imperial duty to select the loveliest blossoms and tie little silver bells to them, so that passersby will be sure to admire them.

TRAVELER 2: We congratulate you on such an ingenious plan. Incidentally, just how large are the emperor's gardens?

GARDENER: How large? Why, they're so large that even I don't know where they end! However, I do know that if you walk far enough, you'll come to an immense forest that extends to the edge of the sea.

NARRATOR: The next day, the two travelers set forth on a journey to learn the extent of the emperor's gardens. As they walked through the forest, they marveled at the beautiful things they heard and saw.

TRAVELER 2: Just listen to those wonderful sounds: the chirping of the insects, the sighing of the wind in the trees, the babbling of the brook. The sound of the silver bells in the imperial gardens is sweet, yet these sounds are sweeter still.

TRAVELER 1: Yes, and just look at those colors: the different hues of the leaves and all the shades of blue in the sky. The gilded porcelain in the emperor's palace is wonderful to behold, yet the colors in the forest are lovelier still.

NARRATOR: The two travelers continued on their way until they reached the sea, where the tall trees stretched their branches over the deep blue water. Standing under one of the trees, they heard a most glorious sound.

NIGHTINGALE: [*song of the nightingale*]

NARRATOR: At that moment, a fisherman and his wife happened by on their way to the sea to tend their nets.

TRAVELER 1: Good day to you both.

FISHERMAN: Good day, sir.

TRAVELER 2: Can you tell us—what is that sound we hear?

FISHERMAN: That, sir, is the nightingale who lives in this forest.

WIFE: Her song is beautiful, don't you agree?

TRAVELER 2: Ah, yes. I would say that in this kingdom of beautiful things, it's the loveliest of all!

TRAVELER 1: You're right, my friend. When I get home, I shall write books describing all the amazing things I've seen. But the place of honor will surely go to the nightingale.

TRAVELER 2: And I shall write exquisite poems about the nightingale who lives in the forest by the deep blue sea.

NARRATOR: In time, these travelers' books and poems went all over the world. Eventually, some of them reached the emperor himself! He sat on his golden throne reading and nodding his head over the glowing descriptions of his palace and its grounds.

Macmillan/McGraw-Hill

EMPEROR: Ah, yes, this writer says the porcelain in my palace cannot be matched anywhere in the world.

EMPRESS: How true, my husband, how true. And this poet mentions that the palace seems to glow like a million fireflies when it is lit by lantern light.

EMPEROR: As indeed it does! But what's this? This writer says, "The nightingale is the loveliest thing of all." What nightingale? No one has ever told me of any nightingale! Instead, I have to read about her in a book! Courtier, send my chamberlain to me immediately.

NARRATOR: The chamberlain was the emperor's gentleman-in-waiting. He was so grand that if anyone of lower rank spoke to him, he only answered "Peh!"—which means nothing at all.

CHAMBERLAIN: You wished to see me, Your Imperial Majesty?

EMPEROR: I have just read in this very learned book that a remarkable bird called a nightingale lives in my garden. Why haven't you told me about her?

CHAMBERLAIN: Nightingale, Your Majesty? I've never heard that name. I'm sure she has never been presented at court.

EMPEROR: Well, I command you to bring her here to sing for me tonight. Imagine, the whole world knows that I possess this marvel, yet *I* know nothing of her!

CHAMBERLAIN: This is the first time I've heard of her. But if she exists, she shall be found and brought to you.

NARRATOR: The chamberlain had no idea where to begin looking. He ran upstairs and then downstairs. He ran through all the rooms and corridors of the palace, asking all he met if they had heard of the nightingale. But no one had.

CHAMBERLAIN: Your Majesty, the story of the nightingale must have been invented by the writer. Perhaps you should not believe everything you read. Much of it is made up for people's entertainment.

EMPEROR: But I read it in a book sent to me by the mighty emperor of Japan. Therefore, it must be true! I insist on hearing the nightingale sing this very evening! If she does not appear, every courtier shall be held responsible!

Macmillan/McGraw-Hill

NARRATOR: Again, the chamberlain ran upstairs and downstairs and through all the rooms and corridors. This time, half the court went with him, for no one wanted to be held responsible by the emperor! They asked everyone about the nightingale. To their dismay, it seemed that the bird was known the world over—except to the people at court! At last they came to the imperial kitchen, where they found a young kitchen maid scrubbing the pots.

COURTIER 1: We've been all over the palace seeking information about a nightingale who is said to live in the imperial gardens.

COURTIER 2: Do you know anything about such a bird?

KITCHEN MAID: Yes, indeed; I know the nightingale. Every evening, I'm allowed to take table scraps to my sick mother, who lives near the sea. As I walk through the forest, I often hear the nightingale. Her song is so lovely it brings tears to my eyes.

CHAMBERLAIN: Little kitchen maid, if you lead us to the nightingale, I, personally, will see to it that you are given a permanent place in the imperial kitchen. Furthermore, you will be allowed to watch the emperor dine!

NARRATOR: So the kitchen maid, the chamberlain, and half the court set out for the forest where the nightingale lived. As they walked, they paused to admire the sights and sounds of the forest. Its wild beauty was so different from the manicured perfection that surrounded them at the palace. When they had gone some distance, they heard a cow mooing.

LADY 1: Ah, there she is!

LADY 2: My, my, what a strong voice for such a small creature!

COURTIER 2: That's strange! I'm sure I've heard her before.

KITCHEN MAID: Why, that's not the nightingale. It's only a cow mooing. We still have a long way to go.

NARRATOR: Then they heard some frogs croaking in a pond.

COURTIER 1: Listen! There she is!

LADY 1: Lovely! Her voice is like little bells.

KITCHEN MAID: No, those are frogs you hear. But it won't be long now.

NIGHTINGALE: [*song of the nightingale*]

KITCHEN MAID: There, that's the nightingale! She's on that branch.

CHAMBERLAIN: Really? I never pictured her so . . . well . . . so small and gray and ordinary. Ah, well, perhaps being surrounded by so many distinguished members of the imperial court has caused her color to fade away.

KITCHEN MAID: Little Nightingale, our gracious emperor would like to hear you sing.

NIGHTINGALE: It would be my pleasure.

CHAMBERLAIN: Most excellent singer, I have the honor to command you to appear at court this evening. There you will entertain His Imperial Majesty with your enchanting song.

NIGHTINGALE: My song sounds best out in the open; here the music is free to go wherever the breezes may carry it. But since the emperor wishes it, I will accompany you to the palace.

NARRATOR: At the palace, everything was scrubbed and polished for the occasion. Flowers hung with tiny bells were placed in all the corridors. With all the comings and goings, the bells jingled and jangled so that the people had to shout to be heard.

EMPEROR: Is everything ready? Where's the golden perch for the nightingale?

EMPRESS: Why, it's been placed beside your golden throne.

EMPEROR: Good. Let the court enter.

NARRATOR: The entire court, dressed in their finest robes, assembled to hear the nightingale. Even the little kitchen maid, now assistant to the imperial cook, listened from the doorway. All eyes were on the nightingale. When the emperor nodded his head, the little gray bird began to sing.

NIGHTINGALE: [*song of the nightingale*]

NARRATOR: She sang so beautifully that tears came to the emperor's eyes and rolled down his cheeks.

EMPEROR: Little Nightingale, you have melted my heart. You shall have my golden slipper to wear around your neck.

NIGHTINGALE: Thank you, but Your Majesty has rewarded me enough. I've seen the tears in your eyes, and nothing could be more precious to me.

NARRATOR: And with that, the nightingale began to sing again. What a success she was! From that day on, she was compelled to remain at court. In addition to her golden perch, she had a golden cage of her very own. And twice each day and once each night she was allowed to go out, accompanied by twelve servants. Each servant held a silk ribbon attached to the nightingale's legs.

NIGHTINGALE: The emperor is kind and generous, for my golden cage is surely worth a fortune. Yet to a wild creature, a golden cage is but a gilded cell, and my twelve servants might as well be twelve prison guards. How I long for the freedom of the forest!

NARRATOR: Life went on this way until one day a large parcel arrived at the palace. The word "Nightingale" was carefully written on the outside.

MESSENGER: Your Imperial Majesty, I bring you this gift from the emperor of Japan.

EMPEROR: Perhaps it's another book about my famous nightingale. Here, let me open it.

NARRATOR: But it wasn't a book at all. There, lying in a velvet case, was a mechanical nightingale. It looked exactly like a real bird, but instead of feathers it was covered with gold and silver studded with diamonds, rubies, and sapphires. The entire court let out a single gasp of amazement and pleasure.

CHAMBERLAIN: Here is the key, Your Majesty. If you please, I will wind it up.

JEWELED BIRD: [*mechanical bird song*]

EMPRESS: How lovely! It's singing one of the nightingale's songs.

LADY 2: See how its tail moves up and down as it sings.

EMPEROR: What a thoughtful gift. Where is the messenger who brought it?

MESSENGER: Here I am, Your Royal Majesty.

EMPEROR: For your part in bringing me this gift, I bestow upon you the title of Chief Imperial Nightingale-Bringer. Now, let's hear both nightingales sing together.

EMPRESS: Yes! What a duet that will be!

NARRATOR: So the two birds sang together, but the duet was not a success. The real nightingale sang freely in her own way, while the mechanical bird sang like clockwork.

EMPEROR: Music Master, the birds don't sing well together. Can you explain why that is so?

MUSIC MASTER: The new bird is certainly not at fault, Your Majesty. It keeps absolutely perfect time. What's more, it sings as if I had taught it myself.

NARRATOR: So after that, the jeweled bird sang by itself. It was just as popular with the court as the real bird. Besides, it was much prettier to look at.

JEWELED BIRD: [*mechanical bird song*]

NARRATOR: It sang its one and only song over and over again—thirty-three times by the chamberlain's count—without tiring. While everyone nodded their heads in time to the song, the real nightingale flew unnoticed to the window.

NIGHTINGALE: I will give up my place to the jeweled bird. Since it is not a living thing, it will not mind a gilded cage. And its song will sound the same no matter where it is. As for me, I will return to the freedom of my forest home.

NARRATOR: With that, the nightingale flew away from the porcelain palace, away from the golden cage, and away from the twelve servants with silk ribbons. Just then, the emperor recalled the other songster.

EMPEROR: Now it's time for my real nightingale to sing. Nightingale! Nightingale? Where is she?

CHAMBERLAIN: Why, she's gone! She must have flown out the open window.

EMPRESS: The ungrateful bird!

COURTIER 1: And after all the favors she has received here at court!

CHAMBERLAIN: Fortunately, you still have the better bird, Your Majesty.

MUSIC MASTER: The chamberlain is right, Your Imperial Majesty. You see, with the real nightingale, you never know what you will hear. But with the mechanical bird, everything has been set beforehand. With this bird, there are no surprises; you always know exactly what it will sing.

ENTIRE COURT: Yes, yes, you're so right!

NARRATOR: The next day, the emperor commanded the music master to display the mechanical bird to the public. The fisherman and his wife were in the crowd.

WIFE: It certainly *looks* very pretty. And it sounds . . . well . . . almost like the real nightingale.

FISHERMAN: You're right, wife, it *is* a good imitation. Still, something is missing. Unlike this mechanical bird, I never knew exactly how the nightingale would sound. There was always something fresh and surprising in her song. Despite the mechanical bird's beauty, I prefer the drab little nightingale's song.

NARRATOR: But the opinion of the fisherman carried no weight, and soon after the arrival of the mechanical bird, the emperor banished the real nightingale from his empire. He kept the jeweled bird on a silk cushion by his bed and raised its title to Chief Imperial Bedside-Singer. A year passed. Then one evening, as the emperor sat listening to the bird, something terrible happened.

JEWELED BIRD: [*mechanical bird song, followed by R-R-R-R-r-r-r-. . .*]

EMPEROR: What's wrong?

EMPRESS: Something cracked!

CHAMBERLAIN: Something snapped!

EMPEROR: Send for the court physician immediately!

NARRATOR: The court physician could do nothing, so the imperial watchmaker was summoned. After a lengthy examination and a great deal of painstaking labor, he was able to get the bird to work again.

WATCHMAKER: I have managed to repair the mechanism, Your Imperial Majesty, but the cogs are worn and cannot be replaced. The jeweled bird will sing, but its song will never sound exactly the same as it once did. Furthermore, I must regretfully suggest that it mustn't be wound too often. To protect the mechanism, I recommend that it be allowed to sing only once a year.

EMPEROR: Only once a year! Well, if it must be, it must be. It is still the finest songbird in my empire.

NARRATOR: Five years passed, and in all that time the jeweled bird sang only five times. But even then, it was almost too much of a strain. At the end of that time, a great sadness fell on the land. The emperor grew so ill it was said he would not live. People stood in the street, waiting to hear about his condition. When they asked the chamberlain, he only shook his head.

CHAMBERLAIN: Things look very grave indeed for the emperor.

NARRATOR: A new emperor was chosen, and all the court hastened to pay their respects to him. Meanwhile, the old emperor lay alone in his magnificent bed hung with velvet curtains and golden tassels. Through an open window, the moon shone down on him and the jeweled bird at his bedside.

EMPEROR: I feel so cold and alone. . . . . Music! I need music to cheer me. Little golden bird, I implore you; sing to me. I have given you precious stones and have even hung my golden slipper around your neck. Sing! Sing!

NARRATOR: But with no one to wind it up, the bird was silent. Suddenly, the sound of a beautiful song floated through the emperor's open window.

NIGHTINGALE: [*song of the nightingale*]

EMPEROR: Nightingale? . . . Nightingale, is that really you?

NIGHTINGALE: Yes, I heard of your illness and came to bring you hope and joy.

EMPEROR: Oh, Nightingale, thank you! I banished you, yet you have come back to comfort me. How can I ever repay you?

NIGHTINGALE: You have already done that with the tears you shed the first time I sang to you. Tears are the jewels that gladden a singer's heart. But rest now. I'll sing you to sleep, and you'll awaken strong and healthy.

NARRATOR: When the emperor awoke, he felt refreshed and well. The sun was shining, and the faithful nightingale was still singing outside his window.

EMPEROR: Dear Nightingale, you must stay with me forever. You may sing whatever and whenever you wish, and I shall break the mechanical bird into a thousand pieces!

NIGHTINGALE: Oh no, Your Majesty, don't do that. The jeweled bird did the very best it could, and it will always be beautiful to look at. Keep it beside you in its accustomed place. As for me, to sing my best, I must live in the forest with the sky as my roof and a nest as my home. But I promise to come every evening of my own free will. I will sit on the branch outside your window and sing to you.

EMPEROR: I see I have been wrong, my friend. You have taught me that a wild creature should not be caged. From now on, it shall be as you wish. You shall be free to come and go as you please.

NARRATOR: Just then, the courtiers came tiptoeing into the royal bedchamber, expecting to find the emperor close to death.

CHAMBERLAIN: Shhh. Be very quiet, everyone.

EMPEROR: Good morning to you all!

COURTIER 1: You're . . . You're . . . up!

COURTIER 2: You're . . . You're . . . well!

CHAMBERLAIN: Your . . . Your . . . Your Majesty!

NARRATOR: From then on, the nightingale returned every evening to sing for the emperor, who lived to rule wisely for many years to come.

BLOCKING DIAGRAM

Arrange eighteen chairs, as shown. The narrator can use a music stand to hold the script.

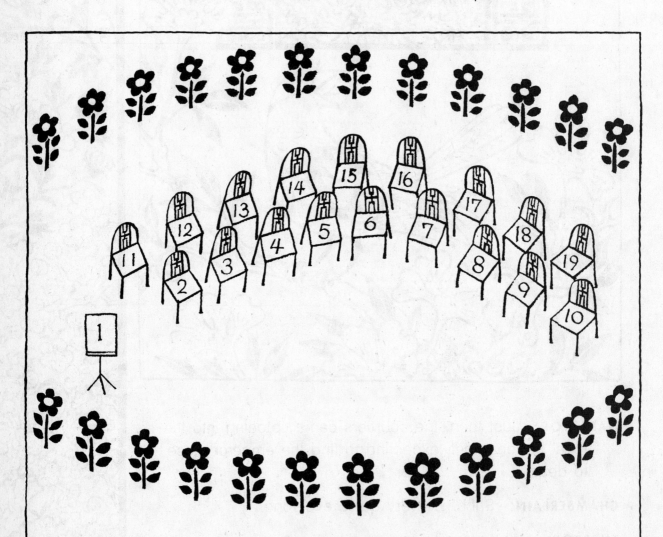

1. NARRATOR	8. KITCHEN MAID	14. MUSIC MASTER
2. TRAVELER 1	9. COURTIER 1	15. WATCHMAKER
3. TRAVELER 2	10. COURTIER 2	16. JEWELED BIRD
4. EMPRESS	11. GARDENER	17. LADY 1
5. EMPEROR	12. FISHERMAN	18. LADY 2
6. NIGHTINGALE	13. FISHERMAN'S WIFE	19. MESSENGER
7. CHAMBERLAIN		

COSTUME SUGGESTIONS

Narrator The narrator can dress as a gentleman or lady of the court.

Emperor, Chamberlain, Courtiers, Travelers, Music Master and Watchmaker The performers reading these parts can wear solid-colored bathrobes tied at the waist with long, colorful scarves. Refer to the illustrations in the play when selecting headgear to distinguish these performers from each other. The Emperor's costume should be the most elaborate.

Gardener, Fisherman and Messenger These characters can wear pants and loose-fitting shirts.

Empress and Ladies Brightly colored bathrobes in solid colors or flowered prints, tied at the waist with colorful scarves, make effective costumes for the women of the court.

Fisherman's Wife and Kitchen Maid The performers reading the parts of these characters can wear long skirts and long-sleeved blouses.

Nightingale and Jeweled Bird

The Nightingale can wear gray pants and a gray turtleneck shirt; the Jeweled Bird should be dressed in colorful pants and shirt. To make bird hats, cut a headband approximately two inches wide and long enough to fasten securely around the student's head. Then accordion-fold two sheets of paper to make wings. Use gray construction paper for the Nightingale and silver or gold foil paper for the Jeweled Bird. Attach the wings to either side of the headband. Glue glitter or costume jewelry to the headband of the Jeweled Bird.

Macmillan/McGraw-Hill

SETTING THE SCENE

Students can create a large mural to serve as a backdrop for "The Nightingale." Use a long sheet of butcher paper and suggest that students include the following scenes: the porcelain palace, the gardens, the forest, and the seashore with the fisherman's boat.

To enhance the story setting, hang Chinese lanterns on either side of the mural. To make the lanterns, fold large rectangular sheets of construction paper accordion-fashion. Then cut slits in the folded sides, leaving one inch at top and bottom. Open up the sheets and glue the ends together. Attach a ribbon loop as a hanger at the top and add tassels made of colorful yarn.

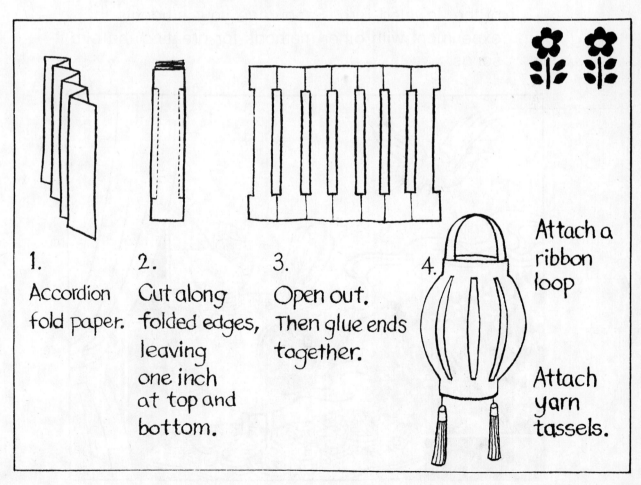

1. Accordion fold paper.

2. Cut along folded edges, leaving one inch at top and bottom.

3. Open out. Then glue ends together.

4. Attach a ribbon loop

Attach yarn tassels.

CREATING SOUND EFFECTS

There are a number of ways to create the bird songs. If possible, have students who can whistle play the parts of the birds. The student cast as the Nightingale can whistle several different songs, while the student playing the part of the Jeweled Bird should whistle one short song repeatedly.

Another alternative is to have a sound-effects operator stationed behind a screen to one side of the cast. This student would create the sounds on cue while the birds on stage move their lips to simulate singing. A plastic, bird-shaped water whistle that makes a chirping sound could be used to create the Nightingale's song, while a wind-up music-box bird could be used to simulate the song of the Jeweled Bird. Encourage your students to experiment with other methods for creating the bird songs.

Macmillan/McGraw-Hill

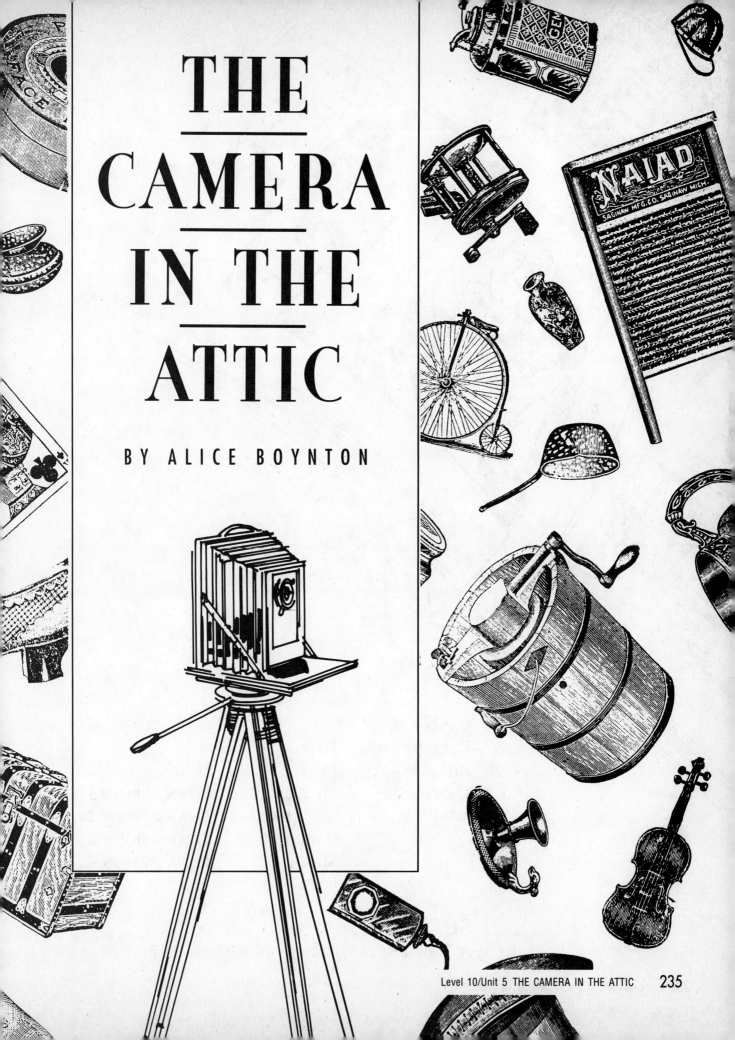

THE CAMERA IN THE ATTIC

BY ALICE BOYNTON

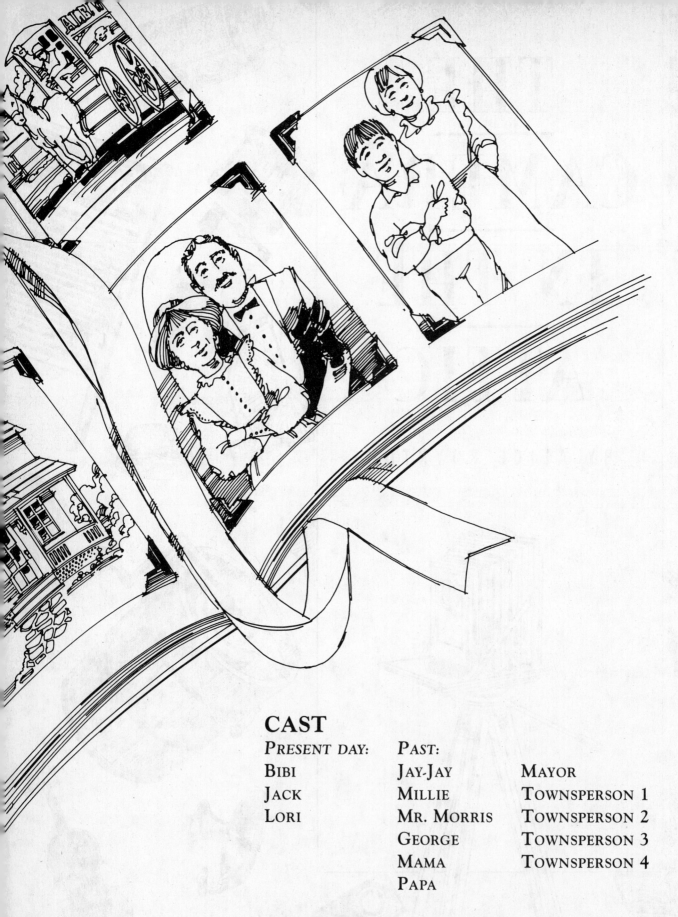

CAST

PRESENT DAY:	PAST:	
BIBI	JAY-JAY	MAYOR
JACK	MILLIE	TOWNSPERSON 1
LORI	MR. MORRIS	TOWNSPERSON 2
	GEORGE	TOWNSPERSON 3
	MAMA	TOWNSPERSON 4
	PAPA	

SETTING

A NEW ENGLAND TOWN, 1990S AND 1875

BIBI: What an awful way to spend the Fourth of July. Just sitting around in Grammy's attic is not exactly my idea of fun.

JACK: Yeah. Why did it have to rain today of all days!

LORI: Well, it's too bad the weather is so uncooperative. But maybe there's something new up here—you know, something old that's new.

JACK: Gee, Lori, we've been up here *so* many times. I can't believe there's anything we've missed. There's Grammy's doll from when she was little, and great-grandmother's high-button shoes. And here's our great-great-grandmother's rocking horse and . . . Hey, look at that. The horse has some initials on it. I never noticed that before.

BIBI: Really? What are they?

LORI: "B.B." Do you suppose you were named after a rocking horse, Bibi?

BIBI: Very funny. Those must have been our great-great-grandmother's initials—"B.B."

JACK: Gee, I wonder if her first name was Barbara? You know, like Grammy.

LORI: Could be. Grammy might have been named after her. See, there *are* things up here we've never seen before.

JACK: I guess that's possible . . . This attic is so crammed with stuff that I guess *anything* is possible.

BIBI: How old is this house, anyway?

LORI: Grammy says it's one of the oldest houses in Johnsbury. It's been here for five generations.

BIBI: Wouldn't that mean it was built when our great-great-grandparents were alive?

JACK: Wow! Talk about old.

BIBI: That would make it more than a hundred years old! Is that right?

JACK: I don't know. You're the math whiz, Bibi. If you say so, that's good enough for me. Hey, Lori, what are you doing now?

LORI: I'm checking out this thing in the corner. It's on some kind of old wooden tripod.

JACK: It looks like an old camera—a *real* old one. It's the kind where the photographer had to get under a hood to snap the picture.

BIBI: Hey, let's set it up. Maybe it still works.

JACK: That old thing? Impossible! Those cameras didn't even use film. They used special glass plates treated with chemicals that recorded the picture. And developing the photograph was really complicated. There's no way you could still use it.

BIBI: How come you know so much about photography all of a sudden?

JACK: Well, maybe one of our ancestors was a famous photographer—and it's in my genes. . . . Where did Lori disappear to now?

Macmillan/McGraw-Hill

LORI: I'm here, under the hood of this camera. This is really weird. I don't get it.

JACK: What do you mean?

LORI: Come see for yourself.

BIBI: Move over, you two! Make room for me under there!

LORI: See what I mean? When you look through the viewfinder, you see something. But it's not the attic. It's a house!

BIBI: Yeah . . . and it looks kind of familiar, too. In fact, if the two trees in front weren't so small, and if there were hedges on the sides, I would say it was *this* house.

JACK: Hey, do you feel as if we're moving?

BIBI: Yes! We're going into the picture!

LORI: Whoaaa! Hang on!

BIBI: What happened? We're not in the attic any more. We're outside! What's going on here?

LORI: Look over there! It's Grammy's house.

JACK: No, it isn't. It's the house we saw in the camera. We're on the front lawn, and here's the camera from Grammy's attic!

JAY-JAY: That's right. So it is.

LORI: Who are you?

JACK: How did this guy get here? He looks like he's right out of the last century!

BIBI: Where *are* we? Where did *you* come from?

JAY-JAY: Hold on! My name is Jay-Jay, and I live here. I have been looking forward to a visit from you. Welcome at last!

LORI: Do you mean you were expecting us?

JAY-JAY: In a way. I've been waiting for you to look into the camera. There is a whole world for you to discover behind the lens.

JACK: What world?

JAY-JAY: Your whole history, you might say. And now you're here, right in the middle of it.

MILLIE: Oh, Jay-Jay—Mr. Morris the iceman is here. Mama has been waiting for him.

LORI: Wait a minute! Where did *you* come from?

MILLIE: Oh, just from across the street. I was over there petting Mr. Morris's horse. I like to give Elsie a lump of sugar whenever Mr. Morris comes by with the ice. She's a real nice horse. And Mr. Morris is real nice, too. Sometimes he even lets me help him drive the ice wagon.

BIBI: Lori! Jack! She's not kidding. There *is* a horse across the street—and a wagon loaded with blocks of ice, too.

LORI: I don't get any of this. Who are all these people?

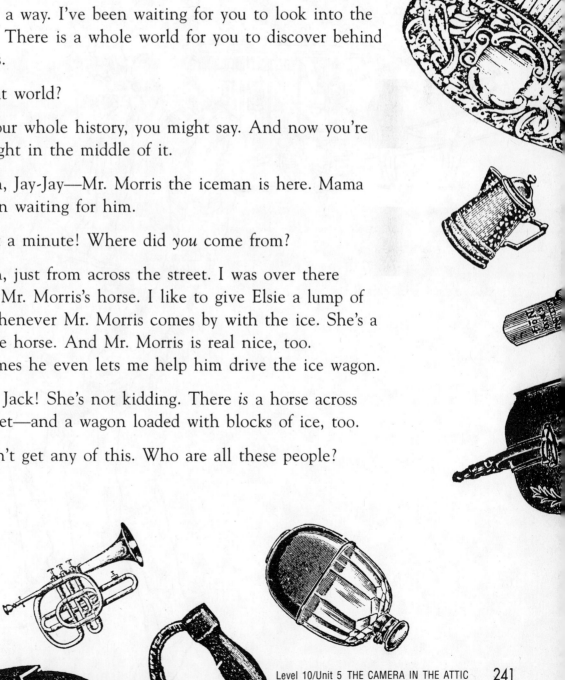

JACK: And where are we?

BIBI: I don't know. It's strange, but it's kind of fun. Who's this?

MR. MORRIS: Good morning, folks. Are you sure you have enough room for all this ice, Jay-Jay? Your ma asked me for a sixty-pound block.

MILLIE: We need the extra for ice cream, Mr. Morris. I'm going to help Mama make it. I volunteered to turn the crank on our brand new ice-cream freezer. We got it just in time for the celebration.

BIBI: What celebration?

MR. MORRIS: Why, the Fourth of July celebration, of course!

MILLIE: We're having a family picnic. That's why Jay-Jay is setting up his camera. He is going to take a picture of everyone in front of the house.

JACK: I'm a good photographer, Jay-Jay. Maybe I can help you.

JAY-JAY: That's the spirit, Jack. Now you're getting into it!

JACK: But I still don't get it.

JAY-JAY: You will!

MR. MORRIS: We had better get this ice into the icebox. It's starting to melt.

LORI: What's an icebox?

MILLIE: What's an icebox? Why, it's a tall wooden box with two sections in it. You put your food in the bottom section and your ice in the top one. The ice keeps the food cold. It even keeps milk from turning sour for two whole days. Don't you have an icebox?

LORI: No, we have a refrigerator.

MILLIE: What's a refrigerator?

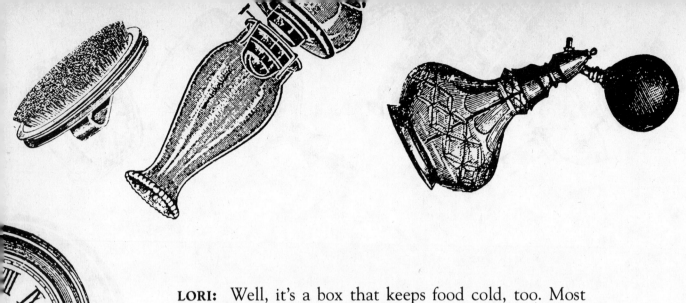

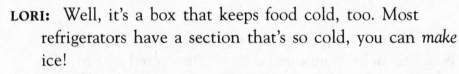

LORI: Well, it's a box that keeps food cold, too. Most refrigerators have a section that's so cold, you can *make* ice!

MR. MORRIS: Well, thank goodness we do not have refrigerators here! They would put me out of business! I had best be moving on. Seems like everyone in Johnsbury wants ice today.

LORI: Johnsbury? Did you hear that? We're still in Johnsbury!

MR. MORRIS: And there's no better place to be on July 4th, 1875—or any other time!

JACK: Did you say *1875*?

MR. MORRIS: Of course I did. Don't you know what year it is, young man? Where do you go to school, anyway?

JACK: Why, I go to school right here in Johnsbury. I'm in the fourth grade at the Thomas Alva Edison Middle School on Blacksmith Road.

MR. MORRIS: I never heard of it. The only thing on Blacksmith Road is the blacksmith's shop.

LORI: Did you hear that? Jack, you know the old iron hitching posts in front of the video store on Blacksmith Road? They must have been the ones that the blacksmith's customers used.

MR. MORRIS: Well, good-bye, all. I'll see you at the fireworks display tonight.

GEORGE: Jay-Jay! You will not believe what I just found out!

MILLIE: Slow down, George. Catch your breath!

GEORGE: I just heard the news down at Wilkins and Sons Confectionery Shop, and I ran all the way here without stopping.

JAY-JAY: That has to be some news, George! What is it?

GEORGE: The bone shakers are coming! They'll be here any minute.

JACK: Bone shakers? Uh-oh! Let's get out of here!

JAY-JAY: No, no, stay and watch. It's fun.

LORI: It is? Who are they, some new rock group?

GEORGE: Did you say rock group? Oh, no. You don't rock them. You ride them. Mama! Papa! Come on out quick! The bone shakers are coming!

MAMA: Here we are!

PAPA: Are they in sight yet?

GEORGE: I can just make them out. There must be at least ten of them.

LORI: Oh, Jack, it's a bicycle club!

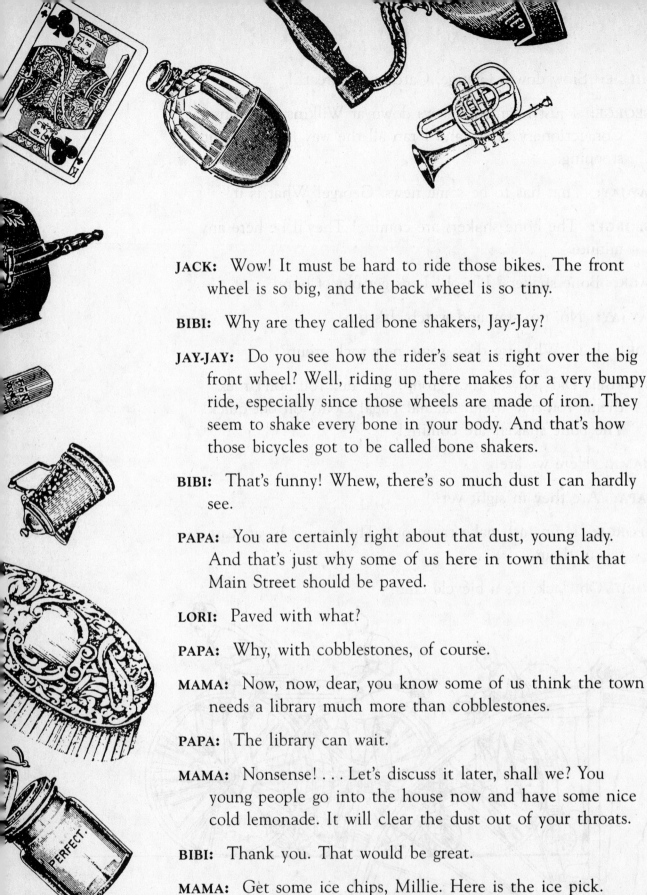

JACK: Wow! It must be hard to ride those bikes. The front wheel is so big, and the back wheel is so tiny.

BIBI: Why are they called bone shakers, Jay-Jay?

JAY-JAY: Do you see how the rider's seat is right over the big front wheel? Well, riding up there makes for a very bumpy ride, especially since those wheels are made of iron. They seem to shake every bone in your body. And that's how those bicycles got to be called bone shakers.

BIBI: That's funny! Whew, there's so much dust I can hardly see.

PAPA: You are certainly right about that dust, young lady. And that's just why some of us here in town think that Main Street should be paved.

LORI: Paved with what?

PAPA: Why, with cobblestones, of course.

MAMA: Now, now, dear, you know some of us think the town needs a library much more than cobblestones.

PAPA: The library can wait.

MAMA: Nonsense! . . . Let's discuss it later, shall we? You young people go into the house now and have some nice cold lemonade. It will clear the dust out of your throats.

BIBI: Thank you. That would be great.

MAMA: Get some ice chips, Millie. Here is the ice pick. Mind how you use it. And George, I will be needing some more coal for the stove. There is still lots more cooking to be done for the picnic.

Macmillan/McGraw-Hill

GEORGE: Yes, Mama.

MAMA: Jay-Jay, please pump up some water and set it on the stove to boil. Your friend here can help you. Be sure there's enough water to fill all the bedroom pitchers. We will want to wash all this dust off.

JAY-JAY: Come on, Jack. I'll show you where the pump is.

LORI: Gosh, Bibi, did you hear all that? Sounds like a lot of work just to be able to wash your face and hands.

BIBI: It makes you realize how lucky we are. Just a turn of the faucet and we get all the hot and cold water we want!

MAMA: What's that you girls are saying?

LORI: Uh . . . just that this is a beautiful kitchen, Ma'am. I saw a picture of one something like it in a museum . . . uh . . . I mean in a book.

PAPA: No doubt it was the latest *American Kitchens Catalog* you saw it in. This is a brand new type of sink, right out of the catalog. Isn't it a beauty?

MILLIE: It's made of iron. If you forget to dry it out after you use it, it gets rusty.

PAPA: That will do, Millie. As I was saying, this is the latest in stoves. It burns coal as well as wood. *And* it has a perfect baking oven. Isn't that right, dear?

MAMA: Yes, indeed.

PAPA: There certainly are a great many new inventions nowadays. And this kitchen is right up to the minute!

Macmillan/McGraw-Hill

MAMA: I half expect that one of these days I'll go to sleep and wake up to find that some new invention has washed all the dishes and scrubbed and dried all the clothes!

LORI: I wouldn't be a bit surprised, Ma'am.

MAYOR: Excuse me, folks, I knocked, but I guess you didn't hear me.

PAPA: Sorry, Mr. Mayor. Come in, come on in. Won't you sit down?

MAYOR: Don't mind if I do. I'm exhausted! I've been out all morning telling people about today's festivities.

BIBI: Excuse me, sir. Why didn't you just call them on the telephone?

MAYOR: The tell-a-what?

BIBI: The *telephone.*

MAYOR: I never heard of any such thing. Well, we'll be gathering on the village green in just a few minutes. Then tonight we will be shooting off fireworks in the big meadow on Duck Pond Road.

LORI: Did you hear that, Bibi? My piano teacher lives on Duck Pond Road right across the street from Livingston Mall.

PAPA: You must be mistaken, young lady. I know everyone in town. There is no one here by the name of Livingston Mall. And there is no one living out on Duck Pond Road, either—except the ducks, of course.

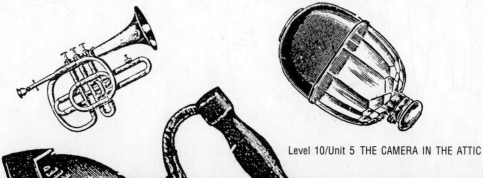

MAMA: But it *is* the main road leading in and out of town. And there are some of us who would be happy to see a public library built right where Duck Pond Road crosses Main Street.

MAYOR: Ahem . . . well . . . uh, I think we had better get going. You are welcome to ride with me. My horse and carriage are right in front. The young people won't mind walking, I'm sure.

PAPA: Thank you, Mr. Mayor. Come along, everybody. Let's not delay.

Macmillan/McGraw-Hill

MAYOR: Greetings, every . . . no, no. . . . Good afternoon, distinguished citizens of . . . no, no, no. . . . Welcome all to . . .

MAMA: What are you saying, Mr. Mayor?

MAYOR: Nothing, nothing. I was just thinking about my speech.

PAPA: Well, I hope you've got it ready because here we are, at the village green!

ALL: Hooray! Hooray!

TOWNSPERSON 1: Three cheers for the mayor!

TOWNSPERSON 2: I hope the speeches aren't too long!

MAYOR: Good afternoon to all you good people of Johnsbury on this glorious Fourth of July! Ninety-nine years ago, these United States became free and independent. Today we are still growing, with thirty-seven states in the Union! And I am proud to say that Johnsbury is growing right along with the rest of America.

ALL: Hip, hip, hooray!

MAYOR: In the past few years, we have witnessed the opening of a shoe factory and a beautiful emporium filled with merchandise from far and wide. Our town newspaper is now published every week! Not only that, it has grown from a single sheet to four full pages. Furthermore, I predict that in the next year, we will see gaslights on Main Street!

ALL: Hooray, hooray!

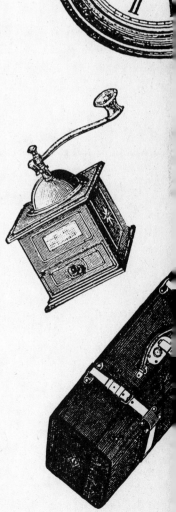

MR. MORRIS: But when are we going to *pave* Main Street? My bones can't take that rocky road anymore. Neither can my wagon. Even my horse is complaining!

TOWNSPERSON 3: Hear, hear! Main Street is the main shopping street in town. But when it rains, we ought to call it Knee-Deep-in-Mud Street! It's bad for business!

MAMA: Many of us feel that it is more important for Johnsbury to build a public library. If we want our children to be ready to take their places as good citizens, they must be well informed. And for that, they must have books to read!

TOWNSPERSON 4: With all due respect, Ma'am, we have got to pave Main Street before we build a public library. Cobblestones are what we need here in Johnsbury, not more books.

Macmillan/McGraw-Hill

MAYOR: Well, maybe this is not the time to . . .

TOWNSPERSON 1: Listen here, Hillsdale isn't even as big as Johnsbury, and they have already broken ground for their public library. Do we want to be behind Hillsdale?

JAY-JAY: And do we want to ride fifteen miles to Hillsdale every time we want a book to read?

ALL: I should say not! No, indeed!

PAPA: But the fact remains that the town does not have the money to build a library, buy books, *and* pave Main Street. We have to choose.

TOWNSPERSON 2: Well, speaking of money, not everyone can afford to buy books all the time. But with a public library, we could *all* afford to read!

MILLIE: That's right! I could borrow Louisa May Alcott's new book—it's called *Eight Cousins.* I would not have to save and save until I had enough money to buy it.

LORI: Oh, Millie, did you read *Little Women?* Didn't you just love it! Especially the part when . . .

MAYOR: Children, children, please! Quiet!

MR. MORRIS: Mr. Mayor, Mr. Mayor! Hold everything! Mr. Jackson down at the telegraph office just received this telegram for you. He says it's urgent. Here it is, sir.

MAYOR: Excuse me just a minute, good people. Let's see what this says. . . . Oh, my . . .

TOWNSPERSON 4: What does it say, Mr. Mayor? Read it out loud.

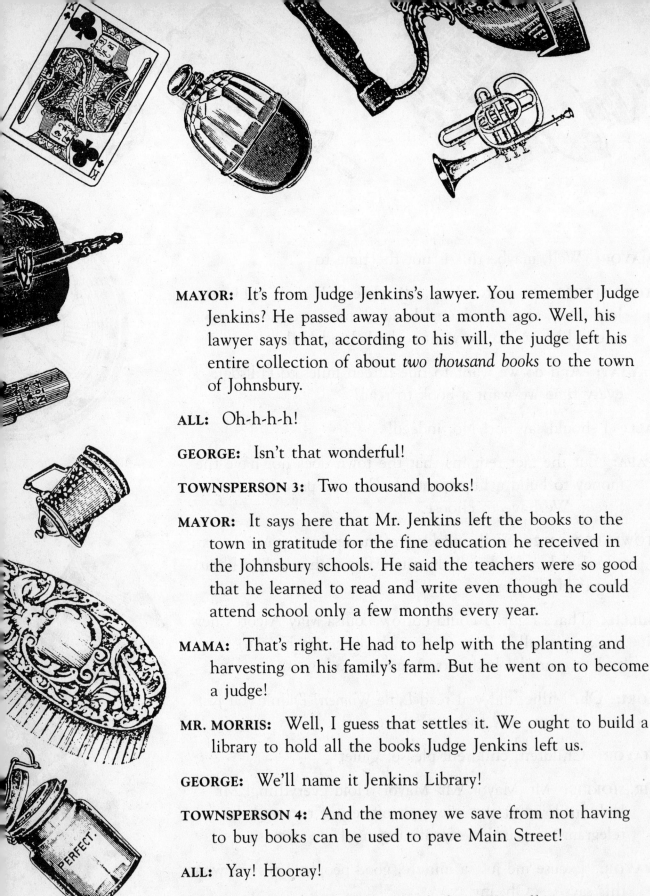

MAYOR: It's from Judge Jenkins's lawyer. You remember Judge Jenkins? He passed away about a month ago. Well, his lawyer says that, according to his will, the judge left his entire collection of about *two thousand books* to the town of Johnsbury.

ALL: Oh-h-h-h!

GEORGE: Isn't that wonderful!

TOWNSPERSON 3: Two thousand books!

MAYOR: It says here that Mr. Jenkins left the books to the town in gratitude for the fine education he received in the Johnsbury schools. He said the teachers were so good that he learned to read and write even though he could attend school only a few months every year.

MAMA: That's right. He had to help with the planting and harvesting on his family's farm. But he went on to become a judge!

MR. MORRIS: Well, I guess that settles it. We ought to build a library to hold all the books Judge Jenkins left us.

GEORGE: We'll name it Jenkins Library!

TOWNSPERSON 4: And the money we save from not having to buy books can be used to pave Main Street!

ALL: Yay! Hooray!

MAYOR: That sounds like a good plan. We will vote on it at the next town meeting. What a Fourth of July this is turning out to be!

JAY-JAY: And just wait until the Fourth of July next year. I just heard that President Ulysses S. Grant issued a proclamation only yesterday. He said that a Centennial Exhibition will be held in Philadelphia in 1876 to celebrate the one-hundredth birthday of the United States of America. Won't that be grand?

MAYOR: Three cheers for Old Glory!

ALL: Hip, hip, hooray!

MAYOR: That's all for now, people of Johnsbury. I hope to see everyone at the fireworks display tonight.

MAMA: Millie, George, Jay-Jay, please gather up your things. It's time to get back to the house.

MR. MORRIS: Excuse me, Ma'am, would you mind if I drop in later on? My niece is visiting. She is studying to be a librarian, and given your interest in the library and all, I thought you might like to meet her. There she is talking to the mayor. Her name is Barbara Blake.

MAMA: We would be delighted to meet your niece. Jay-Jay, why don't you go over to Miss Blake and present her with our compliments.

JAY-JAY: All right, Mother. I'll be home in a few minutes. I want to take that family picture before it gets dark.

PAPA: Good. I will get everyone posed for you.

JACK: Oh, boy, what a day!

LORI: It has been great! But have you two thought about how *we're* going to get back home to our own Fourth of July celebration?

BIBI: Maybe we should talk to Jay-Jay about that.

JACK: Here he comes now. You know, Jay-Jay, it's been a great day, but we've got to be getting home.

JAY-JAY: I know. Don't worry, I can help you. I'll just take the family picture first, since everyone is in place.

JACK: Why don't you let me take it, Jay-Jay. I'm a good photographer—really!

MILLIE: Do let him, Jay-Jay. It will be the first time you've ever been in a family picture.

JAY-JAY: All right. Lori, Bibi, why don't you take a look under the hood, too?

JACK: Yes, come see, Lori!

BIBI: Move over, you two. Make room for me under there!

JACK: Hey, do you feel as if we're moving?

BIBI: Yes, we're going into the picture!

LORI: Hang on! Here we go again!

BIBI, LORI, AND JACK: Good-bye, Jay-Jay! 'Bye, everyone!

JACK: We're back in Grammy's attic!

BIBI: And look—here's Jay-Jay's camera. There's a picture on it.

Macmillan/McGraw-Hill

LORI: No, there are two pictures. Look, this is the picture that Jack took. See? Jay-Jay's in it.

BIBI: And this one is a wedding picture. Oh, my goodness, Jay-Jay is the groom!

JACK: What does it say on the back? The writing is so faded.

LORI: It says, "The wedding of . . . Barbara . . . Blake and Jack . . . Jessup, June 10, 1876."

BIBI: Jack Jessup—that's *your* name, too, Jack! Jay-Jay must have been his nickname! "J. J." Get it?

JACK: I guess I was named after him. I never knew that. You know, he must have been our great-great-grandfather.

BIBI: And Barbara Blake is "B.B." This is *her* rocking horse. That means she was our great-great-grandmother!

JACK: Oh, boy! Jay-Jay was right. We *were* right in the middle of our history.

BIBI: I'm sure there's a lot more family history that Grammy can tell us about.

LORI: There's a lot more Johnsbury history that we can find out about, too. Let's go down to the library tomorrow and look in the town records.

BIBI: You know what? This Fourth of July has turned out to be the greatest!

BIBI, LORI, AND JACK: Hip, hip, hooray!

BLOCKING DIAGRAM

Arrange ten chairs or stools, as shown. The cast members playing the parts of Townspeople can be randomly seated in the audience.

1. BIBI	6. GEORGE	11. TOWNSPERSON 1
2. JACK	7. MR. MORRIS	12. TOWNSPERSON 2
3. LORI	8. MAMA	13. TOWNSPERSON 3
4. JAY-JAY	9. PAPA	14. TOWNSPERSON 4
5. MILLIE	10. MAYOR	

Macmillan/McGraw-Hill

COSTUMES AND PROP SUGGESTIONS

Bibi, Jack, and Lori These three performers can be dressed in T-shirts and jeans or shorts. Since the play takes place on the Fourth of July, they might wear some combination of red, white, and blue.

Jay-Jay A white shirt with a bow tie, light-colored pants, and a vest would be an appropriate outfit for the student playing Jay-Jay.

Papa The student playing the father can wear light-colored pants and a dark jacket over a white shirt. The performer can add a cravat by looping and gathering a dark scarf or handkerchief at the neck and fastening it with a safety pin.

Mama The student cast as the mother can be dressed in a floor-length skirt and a white blouse with a high neck or lace collar. A sash belt could be added to complete the costume.

Millie Millie's dress or skirt should be calf-length. She can also wear tights, dark shoes, and a large bow in her hair.

George George's costume can be a long-sleeved shirt and knickers made by tucking the pants into long socks and "blousing" each leg at the knee.

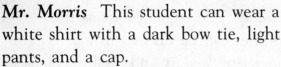

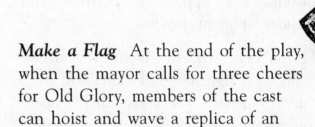

Mr. Morris This student can wear a white shirt with a dark bow tie, light pants, and a cap.

Mayor This performer can use the suggestions for Papa's costume and add a top hat. (You may wish to refer the student to the directions for making Flan's top hat in the costume descriptions for *All the Money in the World*.)

Townspeople The students playing men can wear a variety of caps and hats. Those playing women can also wear hats made by fastening brims of various shapes to basic caps and then adding real or paper plumes, flowers, or ribbons.

Make a Flag At the end of the play, when the mayor calls for three cheers for Old Glory, members of the cast can hoist and wave a replica of an 1875 flag, with its thirty-seven stars.

Macmillan/McGraw-Hill

LET'S CELEBRATE

In the late 1800s, children often made imitation fireworks. You can, too. Here's how.

Thunderbolts Cut a piece of tissue paper into an eight-inch by four-inch rectangle. Fringe one end; then twist the unfringed end. When dropped, the thunderbolts will turn and dart. The twisted side pulls the fringed side down.

Whirls Cut spirals from lightweight paper. Weight them by gluing a small piece of wood to the center. When dropped, the weighted part will pull the paper into a spiral shape.

Sparkling Pipe To make the pipe stem, cut a dime-sized hole about two inches from one end of a paper-towel tube. Squeeze the end near the hole together, and staple it closed.

To make the pipe bowl, cut out a circle with a ten-inch diameter. Fold the circle into fourths, and cut out one section. Then cut off the point to make four or five slits.

Form a funnel by bringing the sides together with a one-inch overlap. Tape the edge. Bend up the slits, or tabs, and tape them around the hole. Cover the pipe with foil.

Half-fill the pipe bowl with confetti or small bits of red, white, and blue paper. Blow through the open end of the tube to scatter the confetti.

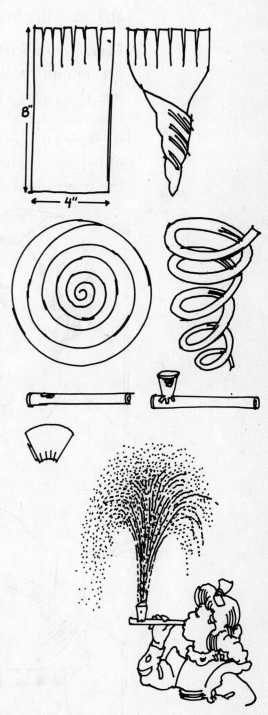

FUN FOOD FOR THE FOURTH

Every holiday has its special foods. Here's an old-time Fourth of July treat that was a great favorite both before and after the fireworks.

Lemon-on-a-Stick Get a fresh lemon and a stick of peppermint candy. Gently roll the lemon on a table to free the juice. Then make a hole in one end of the lemon, and push the bottom of the peppermint stick into it. Suck on the stick as if it were a straw. Small amounts of lemon juice will be drawn up through tiny openings in the peppermint stick. Delicious!

Macmillan/McGraw-Hill

The Way It Was in 1875

Water Pump The endless-chain pump carried many small cups fastened to a circular chain. As the handle was turned, the cups descended upside down into the water, ascended right–side–up scooping up water, tilted at the top, and spilled their water into a spout.

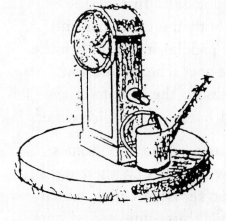

Kitchen Stove This popular model could burn coal as well as wood. Ashes had to be removed before a new fire could be started.

Ice Wagon In 1875, the iceman was probably delivering artificial ice made in an ice plant instead of blocks of ice cut from a frozen lake or pond. The invention of a process to make artificial ice made it possible for a town to have ice on a year-round basis.

Ice-Cream Freezer Ice cream was made by blending milk, cream, sugar, eggs, gelatin, and flavorings. The mixture was put into the freezer container and packed all around with crushed ice and salt. Turning the crank spun both the container and the wooden paddles inside. Salt made the ice melt at a temperature low enough to absorb the heat from the mixture and harden it into ice cream.

Kerosene Lamp Some city homes had the new gaslights on their walls by 1875. But kerosene lamps, which sold for about thirty-nine cents, were still used as a "walking around" light.

Carriage Four-wheel carriages were popular because they had springs, which made a big difference on the bumpy roads of the day. The top could be put up in bad weather. Of course, the driver got soaked!

Kitchen Gadgets Inventors and manufacturers came up with many products to help make preparing foods easier.

MEAT MASHER

BUTTER MOLD

Macmillan/McGraw-Hill

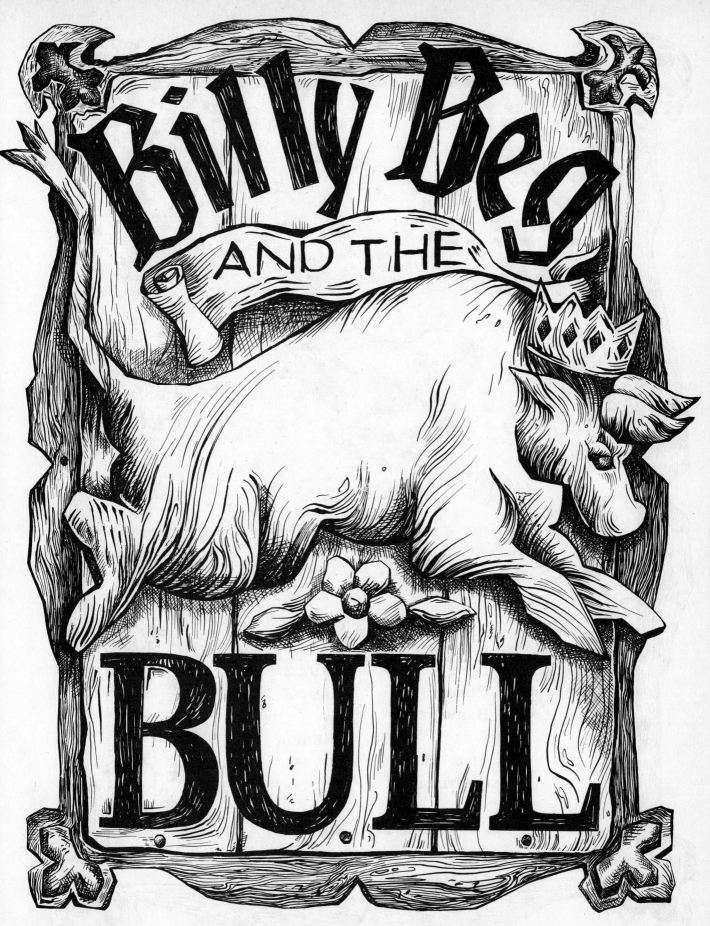

Billy Beg AND THE BULL

by Maggie Palmer based on an Irish folk tale

CAST

NARRATOR	GIANT 1
KING	GIANT 2
QUEEN	GIANT 3
HENWIFE	MAN
BULL	WARRIOR
BILLY BEG	PRINCESS
GENTLEMAN	

SETTING

ONCE UPON A TIME IN IRELAND

Macmillan/McGraw-Hill

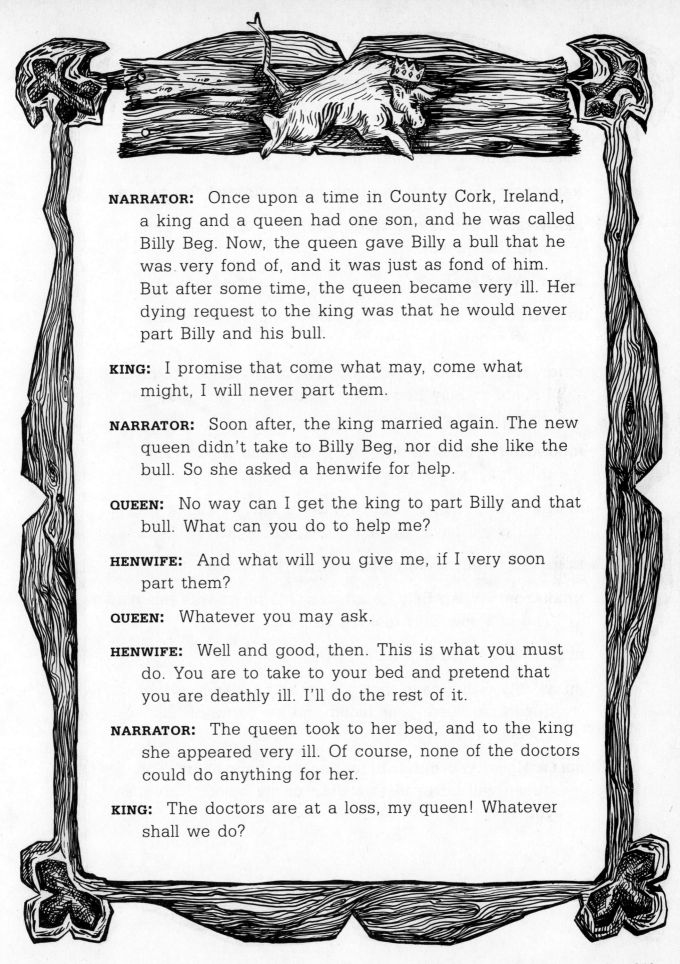

NARRATOR: Once upon a time in County Cork, Ireland, a king and a queen had one son, and he was called Billy Beg. Now, the queen gave Billy a bull that he was very fond of, and it was just as fond of him. But after some time, the queen became very ill. Her dying request to the king was that he would never part Billy and his bull.

KING: I promise that come what may, come what might, I will never part them.

NARRATOR: Soon after, the king married again. The new queen didn't take to Billy Beg, nor did she like the bull. So she asked a henwife for help.

QUEEN: No way can I get the king to part Billy and that bull. What can you do to help me?

HENWIFE: And what will you give me, if I very soon part them?

QUEEN: Whatever you may ask.

HENWIFE: Well and good, then. This is what you must do. You are to take to your bed and pretend that you are deathly ill. I'll do the rest of it.

NARRATOR: The queen took to her bed, and to the king she appeared very ill. Of course, none of the doctors could do anything for her.

KING: The doctors are at a loss, my queen! Whatever shall we do?

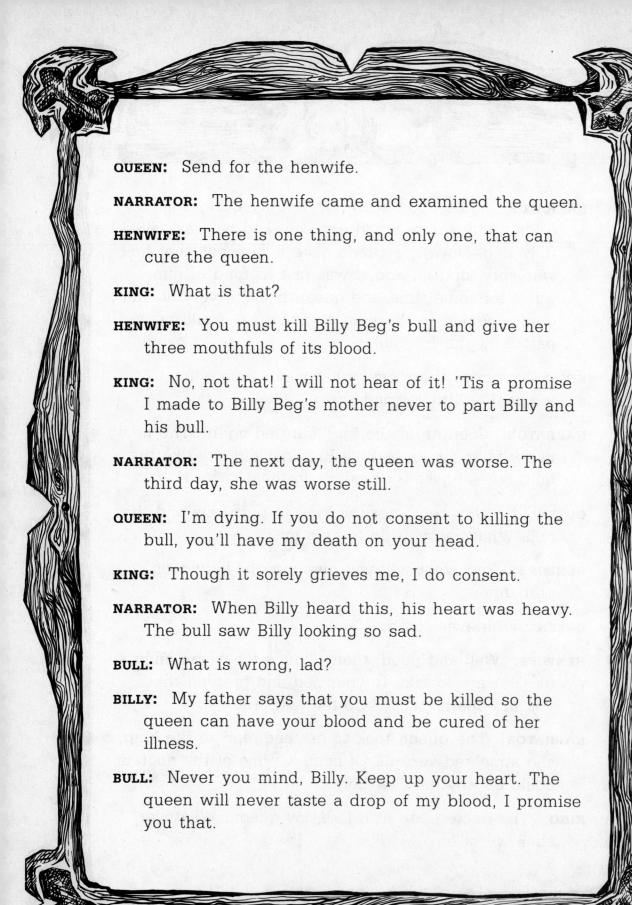

QUEEN: Send for the henwife.

NARRATOR: The henwife came and examined the queen.

HENWIFE: There is one thing, and only one, that can cure the queen.

KING: What is that?

HENWIFE: You must kill Billy Beg's bull and give her three mouthfuls of its blood.

KING: No, not that! I will not hear of it! 'Tis a promise I made to Billy Beg's mother never to part Billy and his bull.

NARRATOR: The next day, the queen was worse. The third day, she was worse still.

QUEEN: I'm dying. If you do not consent to killing the bull, you'll have my death on your head.

KING: Though it sorely grieves me, I do consent.

NARRATOR: When Billy heard this, his heart was heavy. The bull saw Billy looking so sad.

BULL: What is wrong, lad?

BILLY: My father says that you must be killed so the queen can have your blood and be cured of her illness.

BULL: Never you mind, Billy. Keep up your heart. The queen will never taste a drop of my blood, I promise you that.

NARRATOR: The next day, when the bull was being led up to be killed, he suddenly called out to Billy.

BULL: Jump up on my back and let's see what kind of horseman you are!

NARRATOR: Up Billy jumped on the bull's back. And with that, the bull leaped nine miles high, nine miles deep, and nine miles broad. Then down he came with Billy sitting between his horns. Hundreds of onlookers were dazed at the sight. Then, the bull rushed through the castle—right over the queen, killing her dead. Away the bull galloped, over high hills and low, over the Cove of Cork and old Tom Fox with his bugle horn. At last they stopped.

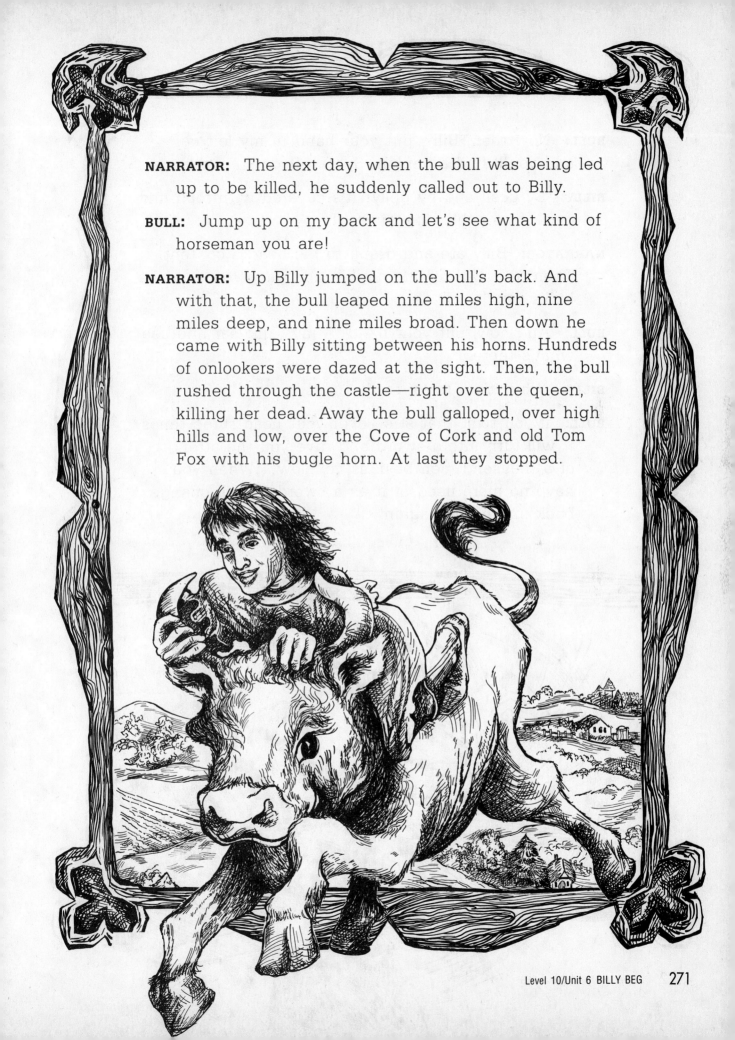

BULL: Now then, Billy, put your hand in my left ear, and you'll find a napkin. Spread it out.

BILLY: By gosh and by golly! It's covered with food and drink fit for the king himself!

NARRATOR: Billy ate and drank to his heart's content. Then he rolled up the napkin and put it back in the bull's ear.

BULL: And now, put your hand in my right ear and see what's there.

BILLY: Why, it's a bit of stick.

BULL: If you twirl that stick over your head three times, it will turn into a sword and give you the strength of a thousand men besides your own. When you have no more need of it as a sword, it will change back into a stick again.

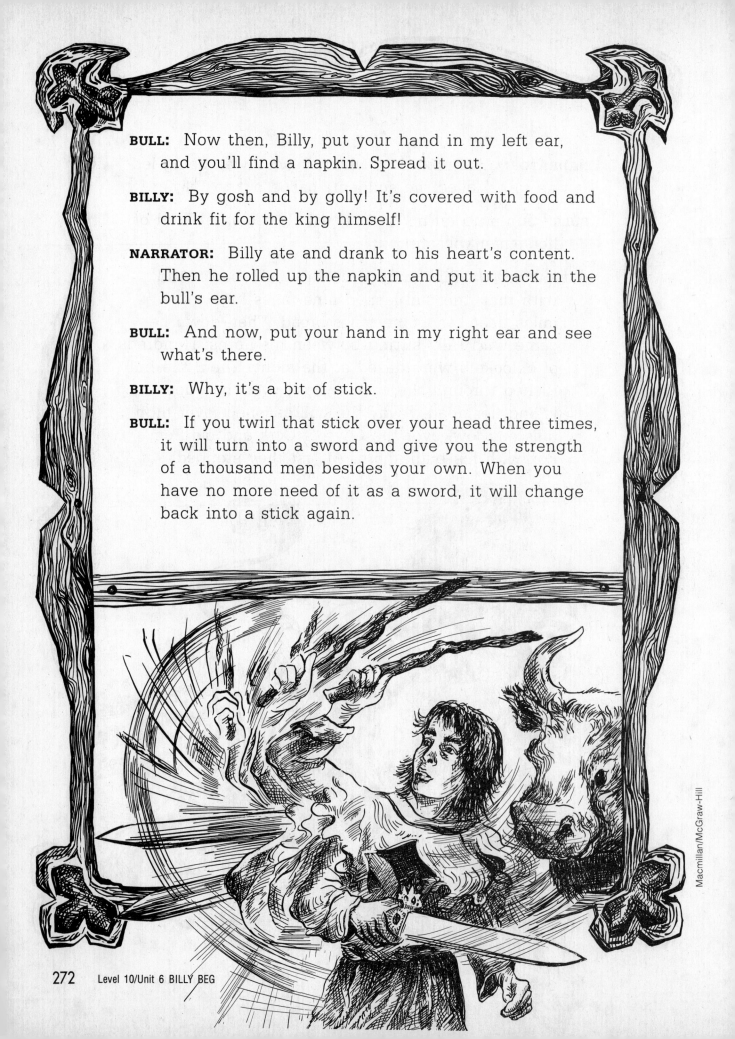

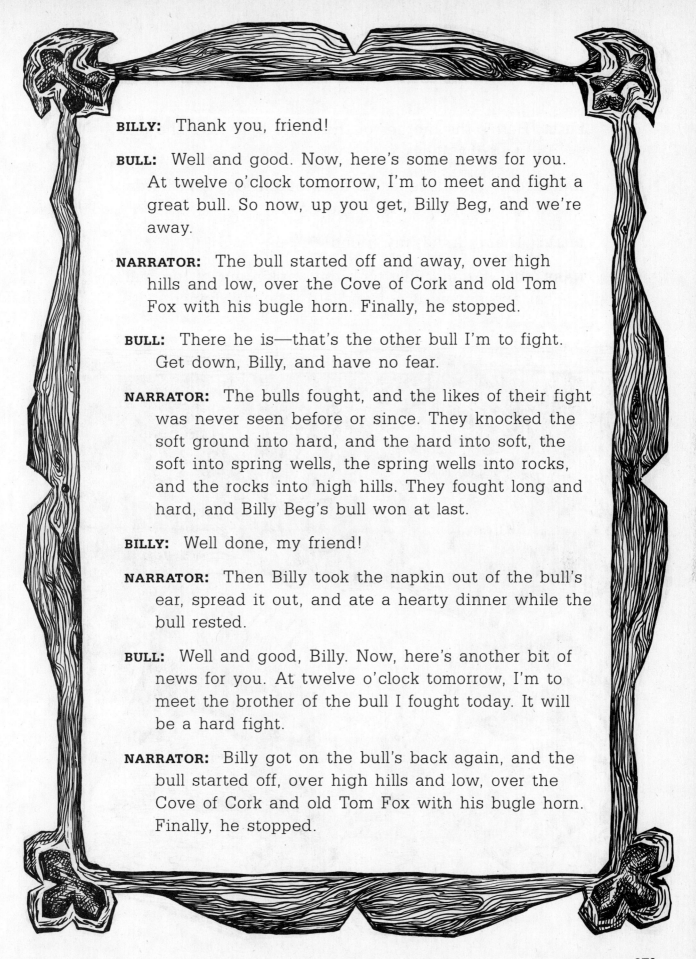

BILLY: Thank you, friend!

BULL: Well and good. Now, here's some news for you. At twelve o'clock tomorrow, I'm to meet and fight a great bull. So now, up you get, Billy Beg, and we're away.

NARRATOR: The bull started off and away, over high hills and low, over the Cove of Cork and old Tom Fox with his bugle horn. Finally, he stopped.

BULL: There he is—that's the other bull I'm to fight. Get down, Billy, and have no fear.

NARRATOR: The bulls fought, and the likes of their fight was never seen before or since. They knocked the soft ground into hard, and the hard into soft, the soft into spring wells, the spring wells into rocks, and the rocks into high hills. They fought long and hard, and Billy Beg's bull won at last.

BILLY: Well done, my friend!

NARRATOR: Then Billy took the napkin out of the bull's ear, spread it out, and ate a hearty dinner while the bull rested.

BULL: Well and good, Billy. Now, here's another bit of news for you. At twelve o'clock tomorrow, I'm to meet the brother of the bull I fought today. It will be a hard fight.

NARRATOR: Billy got on the bull's back again, and the bull started off, over high hills and low, over the Cove of Cork and old Tom Fox with his bugle horn. Finally, he stopped.

BULL: Here's the brother of the other bull. He's the one I'm to fight, Billy.

NARRATOR: The bulls set to and fought long and hard. At last, Billy's bull won the fight.

BILLY: That's grand, my friend!

NARRATOR: Again, Billy took the napkin out of the bull's ear and spread it out and ate a hearty dinner.

Macmillan/McGraw-Hill

BULL: Here's the last bit of news for you. Tomorrow at twelve o'clock, I'm to fight the brother of the two bulls I've beaten. He's a mighty bull entirely and the strongest of them all. He's called the Black Bull of the Forest, and he'll be too much for me.

BILLY: Oh, no, my friend!

BULL: When I'm dead, Billy, you must take the napkin out of my left ear, and you'll never be hungry. Take the stick out of my right ear, and you'll be able to overcome everything that gets in your way. Then take out your knife, cut a strip off my hide, and make a belt of it. As long as you wear the belt, you cannot be killed.

BILLY: Oh, my friend! True, I'll miss you.

NARRATOR: Sure enough, at twelve o'clock the next day, they met the great Black Bull of the Forest. Both of the bulls began to fight, and they fought long and hard. But at last, the Black Bull of the Forest killed Billy Beg's bull. Billy was so sad that for two days he neither ate nor drank, but cried salt tears all the time. After two days and nights, he stopped.

BILLY: I'll spread out the napkin that the bull gave me and eat, for I'm hungry now.

NARRATOR: Billy ate a hearty dinner. Then he cut a strip off the bull's hide and made a belt for himself. Taking it and the bit of stick and the napkin, he set out to seek his fortune. Well, now, Billy traveled for three days and three nights until at last he came to the estate of a great gentleman in another kingdom.

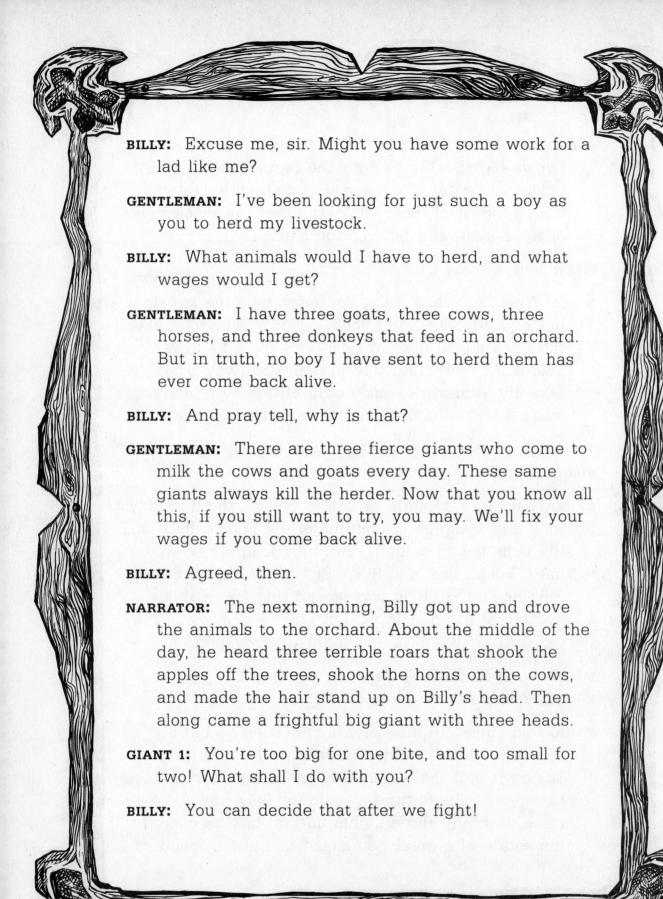

BILLY: Excuse me, sir. Might you have some work for a lad like me?

GENTLEMAN: I've been looking for just such a boy as you to herd my livestock.

BILLY: What animals would I have to herd, and what wages would I get?

GENTLEMAN: I have three goats, three cows, three horses, and three donkeys that feed in an orchard. But in truth, no boy I have sent to herd them has ever come back alive.

BILLY: And pray tell, why is that?

GENTLEMAN: There are three fierce giants who come to milk the cows and goats every day. These same giants always kill the herder. Now that you know all this, if you still want to try, you may. We'll fix your wages if you come back alive.

BILLY: Agreed, then.

NARRATOR: The next morning, Billy got up and drove the animals to the orchard. About the middle of the day, he heard three terrible roars that shook the apples off the trees, shook the horns on the cows, and made the hair stand up on Billy's head. Then along came a frightful big giant with three heads.

GIANT 1: You're too big for one bite, and too small for two! What shall I do with you?

BILLY: You can decide that after we fight!

Macmillan/McGraw-Hill

NARRATOR: Billy twirled the bit of stick three times over his head. The stick changed into a sword and gave him the strength of a thousand men besides his own.

GIANT 1: Well, how will I finish you? Will it be by swinging you around above my head or by a cut of the sword?

BILLY: By swinging me around, if you can!

NARRATOR: They both laid hold for a wrestle, and Billy lifted the giant clean off the ground. He took up his sword and killed the giant then and there. It was evening by this time, so Billy drove home the three goats, the three cows, the three horses, and the three donkeys. That night, all the dishes in the house could not hold the milk the cows had to give.

GENTLEMAN: Well, this beats me. Before today, I never saw anyone come back alive, nor the cows with a drop of milk. Didn't you see anything in the orchard?

BILLY: Nothing worse than myself. Now, what about my wages?

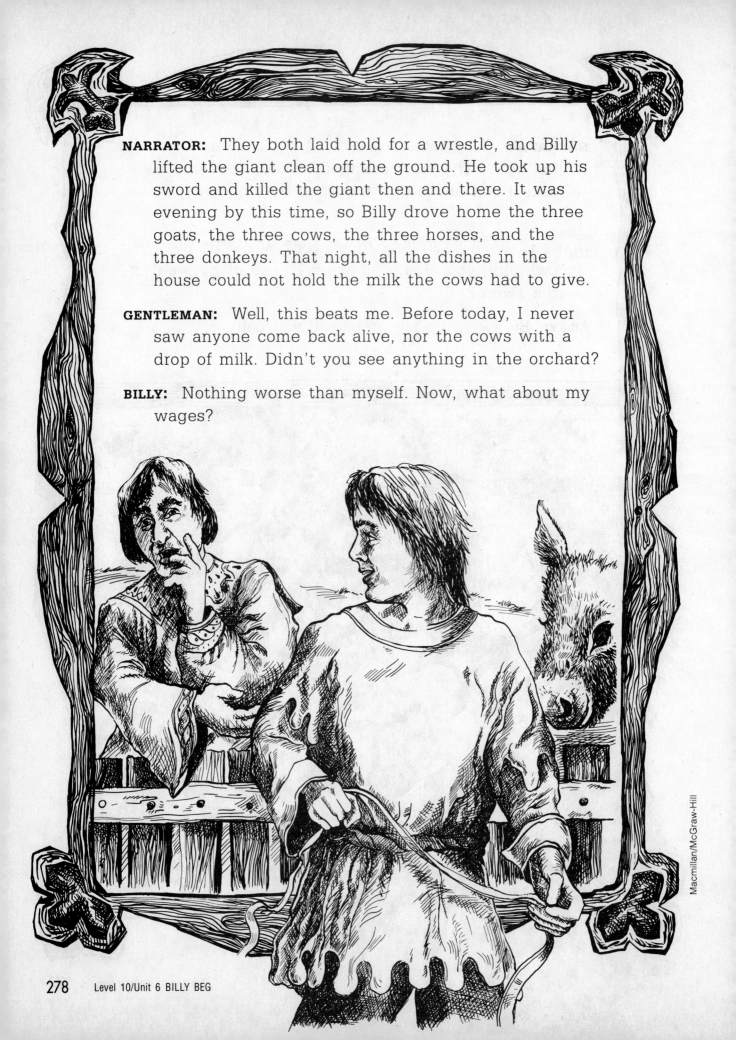

GENTLEMAN: Well, you'll hardly come alive out of the orchard tomorrow. So we'll wait until after that.

NARRATOR: The next morning, the gentleman was puzzled.

GENTLEMAN: Something must have happened to one of the giants. I used to hear the cries of three of them every night, but last night I heard only two.

NARRATOR: After Billy had eaten breakfast, he drove the animals into the orchard again. About twelve o'clock, he heard six terrible roars that shook the apples off the trees, shook the horns on the cows, and made the hair stand up on Billy's head. Then along came a frightful giant with six heads.

GIANT 2: There you are, you miserable lad!

BILLY: What do you want with me?

GIANT 2: I have come to make you pay for killing my brother yesterday! You're too big for one bite and too small for two. What shall I do with you?

NARRATOR: Well, the long and the short of it is that Billy lifted this giant clean off the ground. He took up his sword and killed the giant then and there. It was evening by this time, so Billy drove the animals home again. The milk the cows gave that night overflowed all the dishes in the house and, running out the door, turned a rusty mill that hadn't gone round for thirty years. If the master was surprised the night before, he was ten times more surprised now.

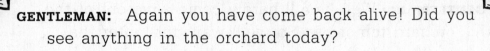

GENTLEMAN: Again you have come back alive! Did you see anything in the orchard today?

BILLY: Nothing worse than myself. And what about my wages now?

GENTLEMAN: Well, never mind about your wages till tomorrow. I hardly think you'll come back a third time.

NARRATOR: When the gentleman arose in the morning, he was puzzled once again.

GENTLEMAN: I don't know what's wrong with two of the giants. Only one did I hear crying last night.

NARRATOR: Well, after Billy had eaten his breakfast, he set out to the orchard once more, driving the animals before him. Sure enough, about the middle of the day, he heard twelve terrible roars. Then along came another giant, this one with twelve heads on him.

GIANT 3: You villain, you!

BILLY: What is your quarrel with me?

GIANT 3: You killed my two brothers! I'll have my revenge on you now. I see you're too big for one bite and too small for two. What shall I do with you?

NARRATOR: Again it ended with brave Billy lifting the giant clean off the ground and taking his sharp sword and killing him with one blow. That evening, Billy drove the animals home from the orchard. This time, the milk of the cows had to be channeled into a valley, where it made a lake three miles long, three miles broad, and three miles deep.

GENTLEMAN: I can't believe my eyes! You're back alive! Did you see nothing in the orchard today, Billy?

BILLY: Nothing worse than myself. What about my wages now?

GENTLEMAN: Well, Billy, you're a good, mindful boy, and I'll give you any wages you wish.

NARRATOR: The next morning, the gentleman met Billy as he was about to go to the orchard.

GENTLEMAN: Not one giant did I hear crying last night. I don't know what has happened to them. Now, Billy, today you must keep a good watch over the animals again while I go off to see the fight.

BILLY: What fight is that?

GENTLEMAN: Why, a fiery dragon is due to devour the king's daughter. The princess will be eaten if the greatest warrior in the land doesn't kill the dragon first. If he succeeds in killing the foul beast, the king's daughter will be his bride.

NARRATOR: The gentleman rode off, and Billy drove the animals to the orchard again. Billy had never before seen the likes of all the people who passed by that day on their way to see the fight.

BILLY: By gosh and by golly! Who'd have thought there'd be so many fine people in coaches and carriages, on horses and donkeys, riding and walking, even crawling and creeping!

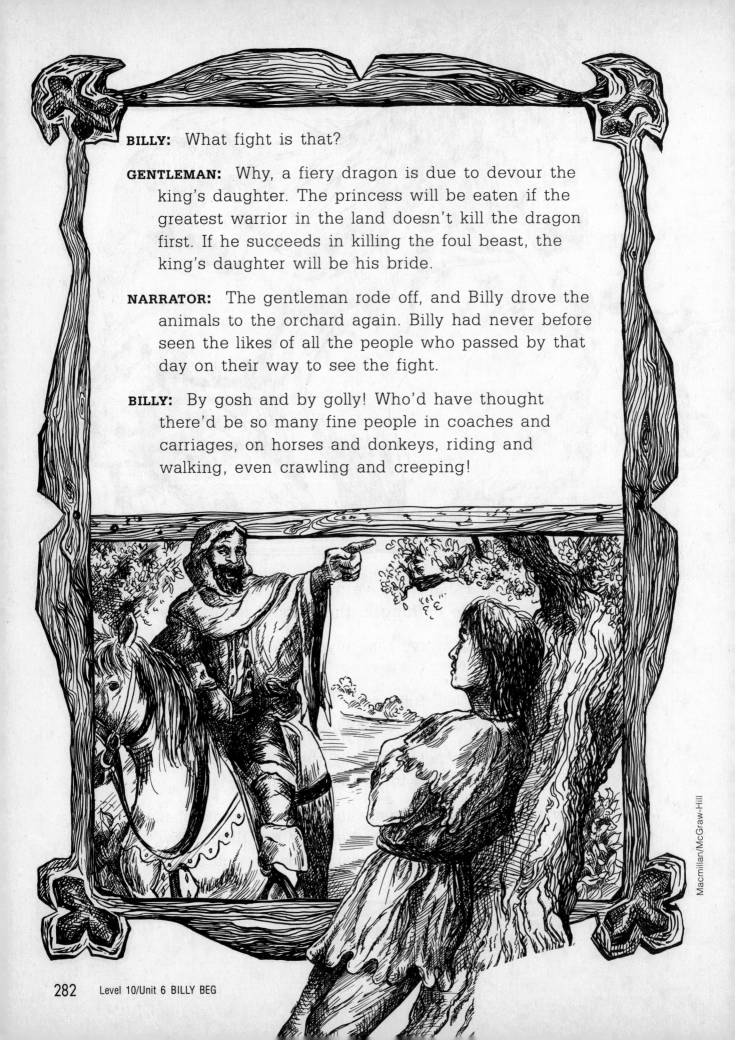

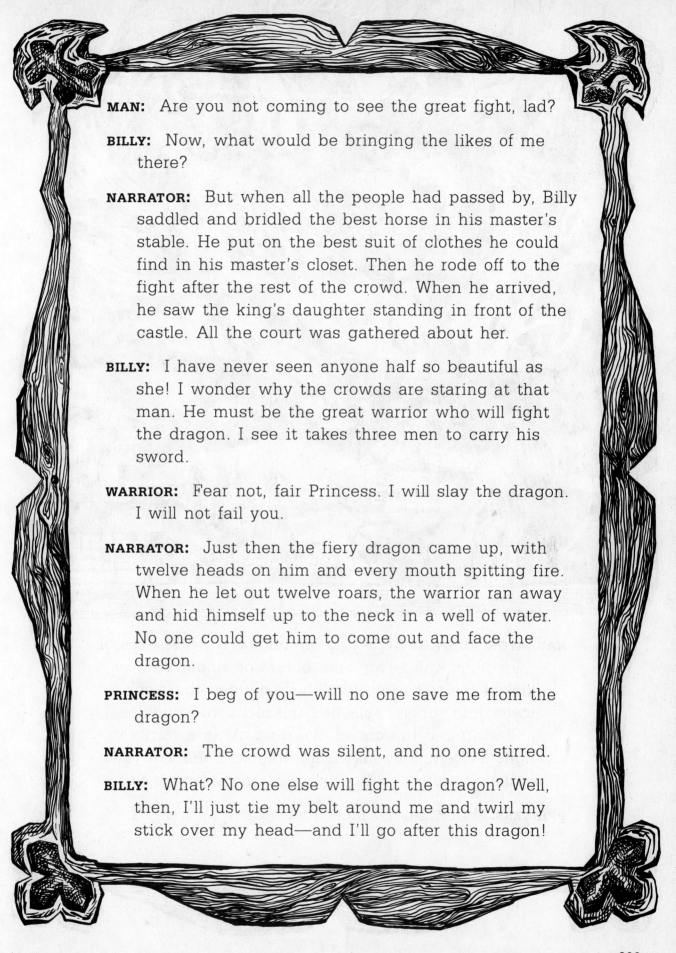

MAN: Are you not coming to see the great fight, lad?

BILLY: Now, what would be bringing the likes of me there?

NARRATOR: But when all the people had passed by, Billy saddled and bridled the best horse in his master's stable. He put on the best suit of clothes he could find in his master's closet. Then he rode off to the fight after the rest of the crowd. When he arrived, he saw the king's daughter standing in front of the castle. All the court was gathered about her.

BILLY: I have never seen anyone half so beautiful as she! I wonder why the crowds are staring at that man. He must be the great warrior who will fight the dragon. I see it takes three men to carry his sword.

WARRIOR: Fear not, fair Princess. I will slay the dragon. I will not fail you.

NARRATOR: Just then the fiery dragon came up, with twelve heads on him and every mouth spitting fire. When he let out twelve roars, the warrior ran away and hid himself up to the neck in a well of water. No one could get him to come out and face the dragon.

PRINCESS: I beg of you—will no one save me from the dragon?

NARRATOR: The crowd was silent, and no one stirred.

BILLY: What? No one else will fight the dragon? Well, then, I'll just tie my belt around me and twirl my stick over my head—and I'll go after this dragon!

NARRATOR: Billy and the dragon fought, and the likes of their fight was never seen before or since. They kicked the trees into kindling, pounded the clock tower into rubble, splashed the moat into puddles, and scattered the crowd like dust. After a terrible fight entirely, Billy killed the dragon. Then everyone gathered around to find out who the stranger was.

PRINCESS: Who is he? I must find out!

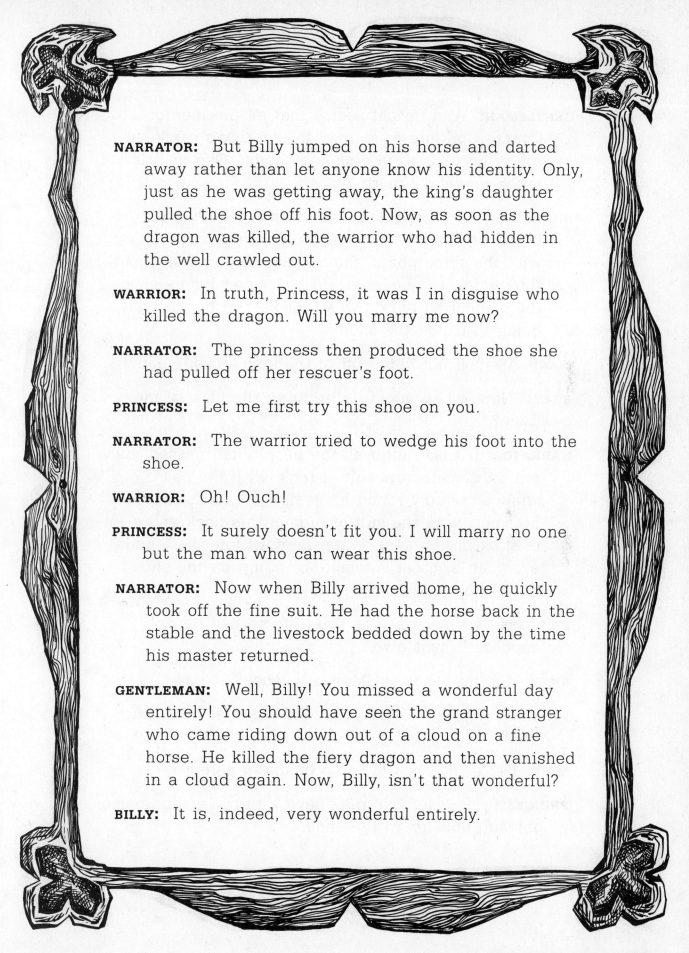

NARRATOR: But Billy jumped on his horse and darted away rather than let anyone know his identity. Only, just as he was getting away, the king's daughter pulled the shoe off his foot. Now, as soon as the dragon was killed, the warrior who had hidden in the well crawled out.

WARRIOR: In truth, Princess, it was I in disguise who killed the dragon. Will you marry me now?

NARRATOR: The princess then produced the shoe she had pulled off her rescuer's foot.

PRINCESS: Let me first try this shoe on you.

NARRATOR: The warrior tried to wedge his foot into the shoe.

WARRIOR: Oh! Ouch!

PRINCESS: It surely doesn't fit you. I will marry no one but the man who can wear this shoe.

NARRATOR: Now when Billy arrived home, he quickly took off the fine suit. He had the horse back in the stable and the livestock bedded down by the time his master returned.

GENTLEMAN: Well, Billy! You missed a wonderful day entirely! You should have seen the grand stranger who came riding down out of a cloud on a fine horse. He killed the fiery dragon and then vanished in a cloud again. Now, Billy, isn't that wonderful?

BILLY: It is, indeed, very wonderful entirely.

GENTLEMAN: And now it seems that all the men of County Cork are to journey to the king's castle so the princess can try a shoe on them. The man it fits is the one she'll marry.

NARRATOR: When the day that the princess had set for trying on the shoe arrived, Billy was in the orchard with the three goats, three cows, three horses, and three donkeys, as usual. He had never before seen the likes of all the crowds that passed by that day going to try on the shoe.

MAN: Are you not going off to the king's castle, lad?

BILLY: Now, what would be bringing the likes of me there?

NARRATOR: At last, after all the people had passed, Billy put on a scarecrow suit of rags, with his belt wrapped snugly round his waist. Off to the castle he went, with the suit of rags on his back and a bit of stick in his hand. When he got there, he found everyone in great commotion, trying on the shoe. Each one tried very hard to get it to fit.

PRINCESS: It's no use. The shoe fits no one here. I suppose I must give up.

BILLY: Let me try it on. Maybe it would fit me.

WARRIOR: Ha! Look at that ragged lad! Get away with you!

MAN: Get along! You have no business here.

PRINCESS: No, everyone may have a turn. Let him come forward and try on the shoe.

Macmillan/McGraw-Hill

NARRATOR: So Billy went up, and all the people looked on, breaking their hearts with laughing. But they stopped soon enough when they heard what the princess had to say.

PRINCESS: Look, the shoe fits him as nicely as if it were made on his foot!

BILLY: I confess it, Princess, it was I who killed the fiery dragon.

PRINCESS: Then you are the man I claim as husband.

NARRATOR: After that, the king had Billy dressed up in a silk and satin suit, with plenty of gold and silver on it. And everyone gave in that they had never before seen his like.

MAN: Well, now, he does look fit for a princess entirely.

NARRATOR: And so Billy was married to the king's daughter. The wedding lasted nine days, nine hours, nine minutes, nine half–minutes, and nine quarter–minutes. And they lived happy and well from that day to this.

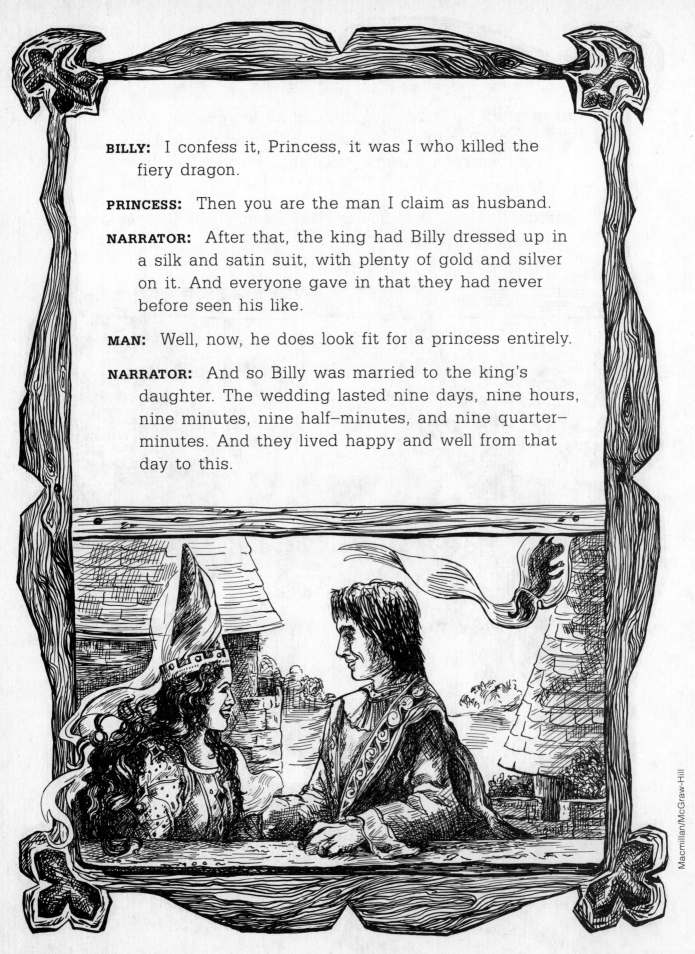

Blocking Diagram

Arrange twelve chairs or stools, as shown. The cast members playing the parts of giants can be seated on very tall stools or on small stepladders. The narrator can use a music stand to hold the script.

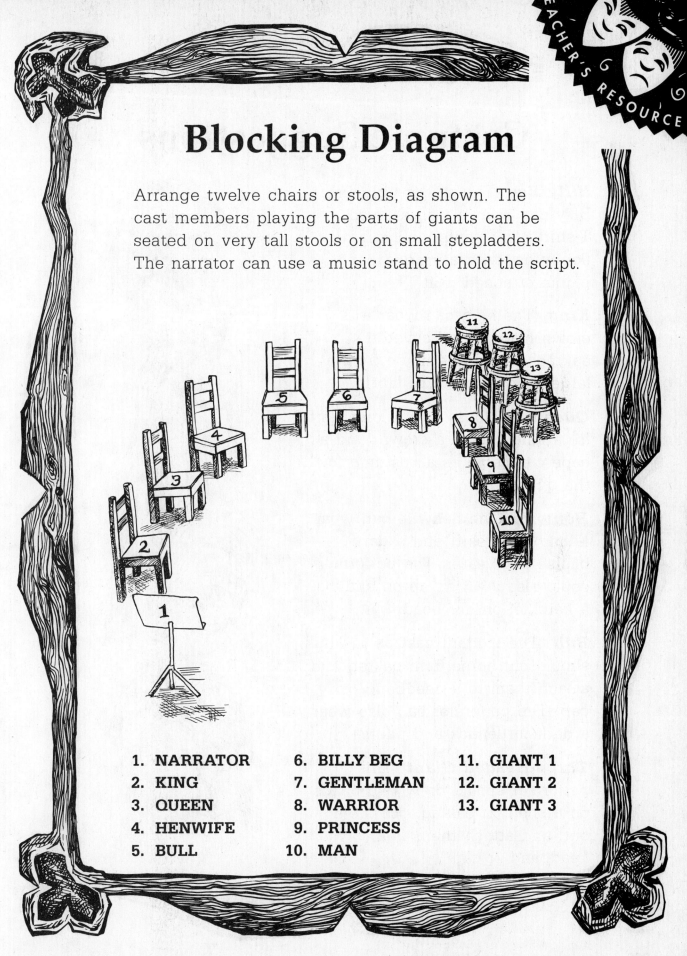

1. **NARRATOR**	6. **BILLY BEG**	11. **GIANT 1**
2. **KING**	7. **GENTLEMAN**	12. **GIANT 2**
3. **QUEEN**	8. **WARRIOR**	13. **GIANT 3**
4. **HENWIFE**	9. **PRINCESS**	
5. **BULL**	10. **MAN**	

Costume Suggestions

Billy Beg The student playing Billy can wear a long-sleeved T-shirt, dark pants, and a large, floppy hat with a fringed paper plume attached to it.

King The king can wear a crown made of foil-covered oaktag and a cape made from a large scarf or piece of fabric.

Queen A blouse and a long skirt (or a long dress), a crown, and a cape can serve as a costume for the queen.

Henwife The henwife can wear a long, dark skirt and a dark blouse or sweater. The performer could also wear an apron and tie a kerchief on her head.

Bull The student cast as the bull should cut horns from oaktag and attach them to a headband or cap. The performer can also wear a dark turtleneck and pants.

Three-Headed Giant This performer should draw two heads on a sheet of oaktag, cut them out, and attach them to a headband or cap.

Macmillan/McGraw-Hill

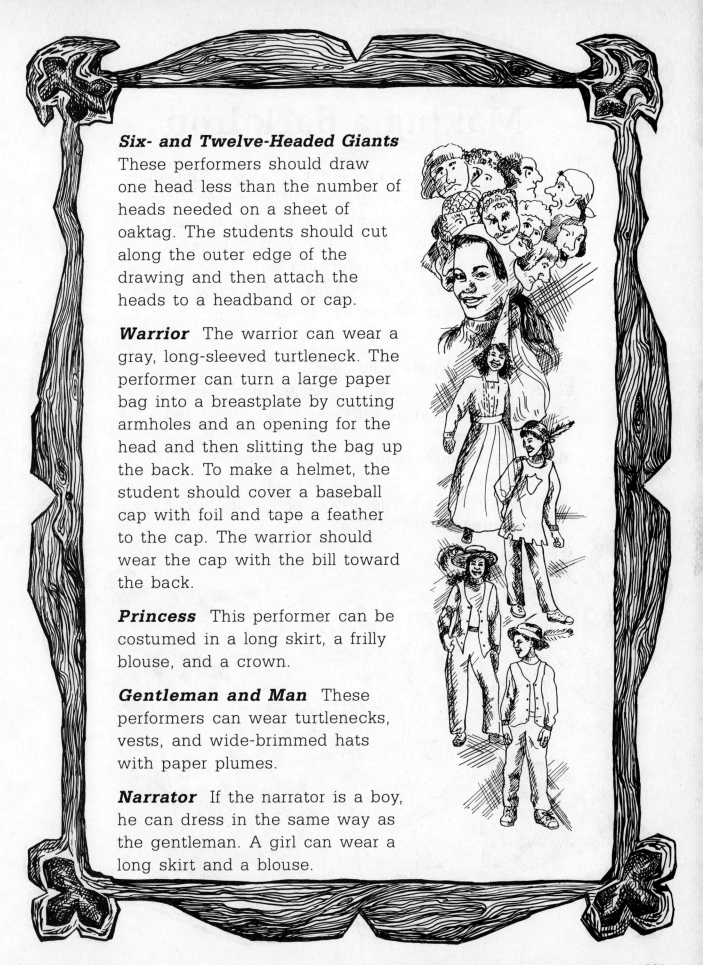

Six- and Twelve-Headed Giants

These performers should draw one head less than the number of heads needed on a sheet of oaktag. The students should cut along the outer edge of the drawing and then attach the heads to a headband or cap.

Warrior The warrior can wear a gray, long-sleeved turtleneck. The performer can turn a large paper bag into a breastplate by cutting armholes and an opening for the head and then slitting the bag up the back. To make a helmet, the student should cover a baseball cap with foil and tape a feather to the cap. The warrior should wear the cap with the bill toward the back.

Princess This performer can be costumed in a long skirt, a frilly blouse, and a crown.

Gentleman and Man These performers can wear turtlenecks, vests, and wide-brimmed hats with paper plumes.

Narrator If the narrator is a boy, he can dress in the same way as the gentleman. A girl can wear a long skirt and a blouse.

Making a Backdrop

A large mural showing different settings within the play could serve as an effective backdrop for *Billy Beg and the Bull.* You may wish to have students use a long sheet of butcher paper, or you may prefer to give individual students large sheets of drawing paper that can be taped together to create the mural. The scenes should proceed from left to right and may include the following settings:

1. The castle where Billy lived
2. A grassy meadow with a stream and trees
3. A large, open field with trampled ground and felled trees
4. A manor house with a fenced paddock
5. An orchard with livestock grazing
6. The princess's castle; a well and a fire-breathing dragon should be visible.

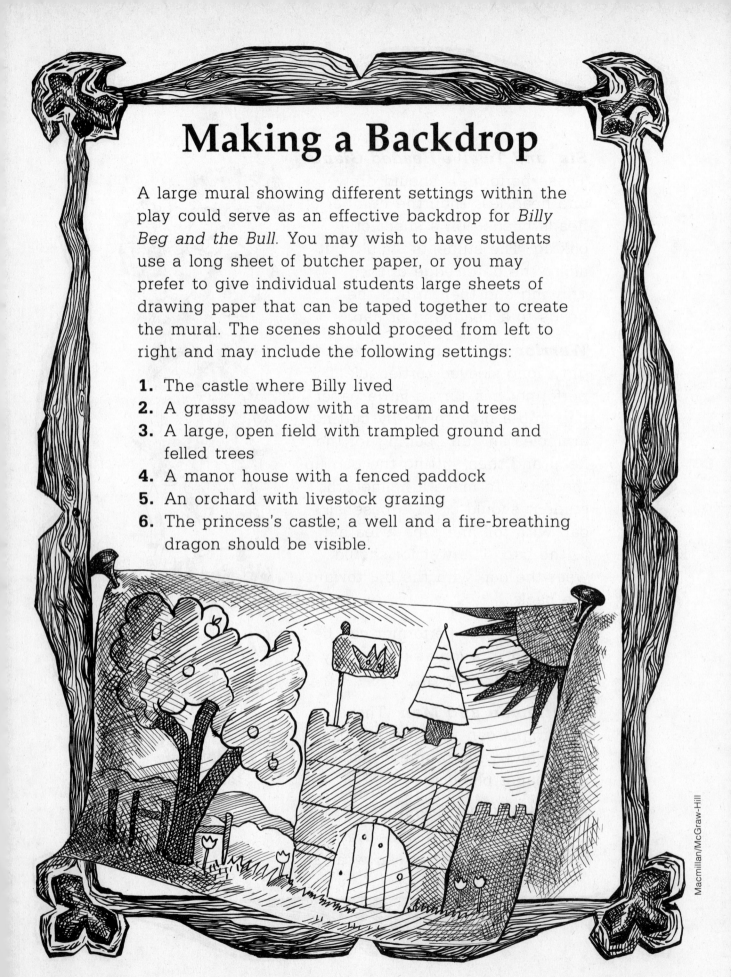

Readers Theater Plays

Once your students have participated in a Readers Theater production or two, many will be motivated to try their own hand at creating a Readers Theater script. The following ten student resource pages are designed to help guide them through this process.

In addition to developing writing skills, creating a Readers Theater script is also a useful way to extend students' study of story elements. In developing any Readers Theater script, students must solve the problem of how to convey action and changes in time and place when the script is read rather than acted on a stage with costumes, scenes, and props. The transformation of narrative into drama also challenges students to closely examine elements of character, motivation, plot, and setting. If students are adapting a story, they must determine what to include and what to leave out. If they are writing an original play, they face a different set of decisions: how to come up with a story line that incorporates dramatic tension and how to make characters believable. If the play is based on historical events, students should determine what research is required to ensure historical accuracy.

Before students begin writing their own Readers Theater plays, you may find it helpful to explore the differences between narrative and drama. One way to do this is to obtain a copy of the novel *All the Money in the World*, by Bill Brittain, or the tale "The

Nightingale," by Hans Christian Andersen. As students listen, read a narrative section from the novel or tale and contrast it with a similar passage in the Readers Theater version found in this book. Discuss how descriptions in the story are transformed into dialog, and how some characters in the play may seem more real because of the words they speak. Point out the role of the narrator in providing transitions from one setting to another and in describing action. Call attention to portions of the story that differ from the play, and invite students to speculate on reasons for these changes.

After students grasp the major differences between stories and scripts, introduce the following Readers Theater writing-process worksheets to guide them through the process of creating their own Readers Theater plays. Students can work individually, in small cooperative-writing groups, or as an entire class when writing a script.

If your students choose to adapt a folk tale or legend, suggest that they read several versions of the tale before they begin the writing process. If students decide to adapt a story or a book, a reading followed by group discussion will ensure that all students are familiar with the story plot, characters, and setting. If students choose to write an original play, they will need to create the plot, characters and setting themselves.

GETTING STARTED

Now it's your turn

Think back to the last time you performed in a Readers Theater play. You may have said to yourself, "I could write a play like this." Guess what—you can! Writing a Readers Theater play is fun and easy, once you know how.

How do I get an idea for a play?

When you are writing a play, your first job is to come up with an idea. Play ideas come from many places. They can come from stories and books, from magazine or newspaper articles, from television or movies, from history, from things that happen to you and your friends, or from your imagination.

Macmillan/McGraw-Hill

Working with a partner or in a small group, brainstorm some ideas for plays. Think of one idea for each source listed. The first one is done to help you get started.

Source	Play Idea
1. Television	Based on a news report about a space probe observing Venus, my play will be about an exciting adventure that takes place on a space station near Venus. There is a problem with the artificial gravity on the station. The crew must solve the problem or face disaster!
2. Book or Story	_____ _____ _____
3. Newspaper	_____ _____ _____
4. History	_____ _____ _____
5. Personal Experience	_____ _____ _____
6. My Imagination	_____ _____ _____

THE PLOT

What is plot and why is it important?

A play is made up of a series of events called a plot. The plot has a beginning, a middle, and an end. Most play plots center around a problem that must be solved. Often this problem is introduced near the beginning of the play. The middle of the play deals with attempts to solve the problem, and the end of the play usually reveals how the problem is solved.

WHAT IS THE PROBLEM?

Macmillan/McGraw-Hill

Here's one possible plot outline for the space adventure idea described on the "Getting Started" page.

Beginning: The crew members of the space station notice something is wrong with the artificial gravity device. Suddenly everything weighs more. They have difficulty moving and performing their daily tasks.

Middle: Several solutions are tried but nothing works. As the problem grows worse, the crew realizes that a shuttle from Earth will not reach them in time. A general S.O.S. message is broadcast and the crew prepares for the worst. The message is received by an underground colony on Venus. The Venusians must decide whether to reveal their existence and help those on the space station.

End: The Venusians decide to establish contact and rescue the crew members. The play ends with a message from the President inviting the Venusians to visit Earth.

Go back to the "Getting Started" page. Select your favorite play idea. Then write a plot outline based on this idea.

1. Beginning _____

_____

_____

2. Middle _____

_____

_____

3. End _____

_____

_____

CREATING A CHARACTER

How do I create the characters?

While your friends and family members may be alike in many ways, they all differ in the way they look, the way they talk, the way they think, and the way they act. The same thing is true of the characters you create for a play—each character is different and very special.

In a play, we learn about characters from what they say and do and from what other characters say about them. So in writing a play, it's very important to have a clear picture of each character.

If you understand the personality of your characters, it will help you to "keep them in character" throughout your play.

How do I write a character sketch?

A writer develops a clear picture of each character by writing a character sketch. Character sketches include what the characters look like, their ages, the clothes they wear, who their friends are, how they are related to other members of the cast, their interests, and their personalities. Here's a short character sketch for the captain of the space station crew.

Macmillan/McGraw-Hill

Captain Nan Butler is a woman in her thirties. She is a former test pilot who has been trained as an astronaut. She is able to think quickly in emergencies and remain calm whatever happens. She is a positive thinker who believes that every problem has a solution. She refuses to give up and is able to help others share her feelings of confidence. Sometimes she gets impatient with people who complain or do not do their best. Her closest friend on board the space station is Jon Walker, the navigator.

Begin by making a list of the characters for the play you have selected. Then write a character sketch for each character. Be as specific as you can. You might want to draw a picture to help you visualize your character.

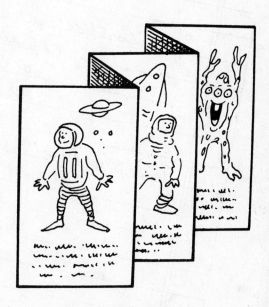

Attach each of your finished character sketches to a piece of stiff paper or cardboard. Then tape the pages together, as shown below, to make an accordion fold-out booklet. Stand the booklet up as you write your play to help you remember each of your characters.

A READERS THEATER SCRIPT

How do I write the script?

Writing a play is different from writing a story. A play even looks different from a story. The characters' names appear on the left side of the page. The words they speak, or the dialog, appears on the right. Here's a portion of the script from the space adventure play described on pages you've already completed.

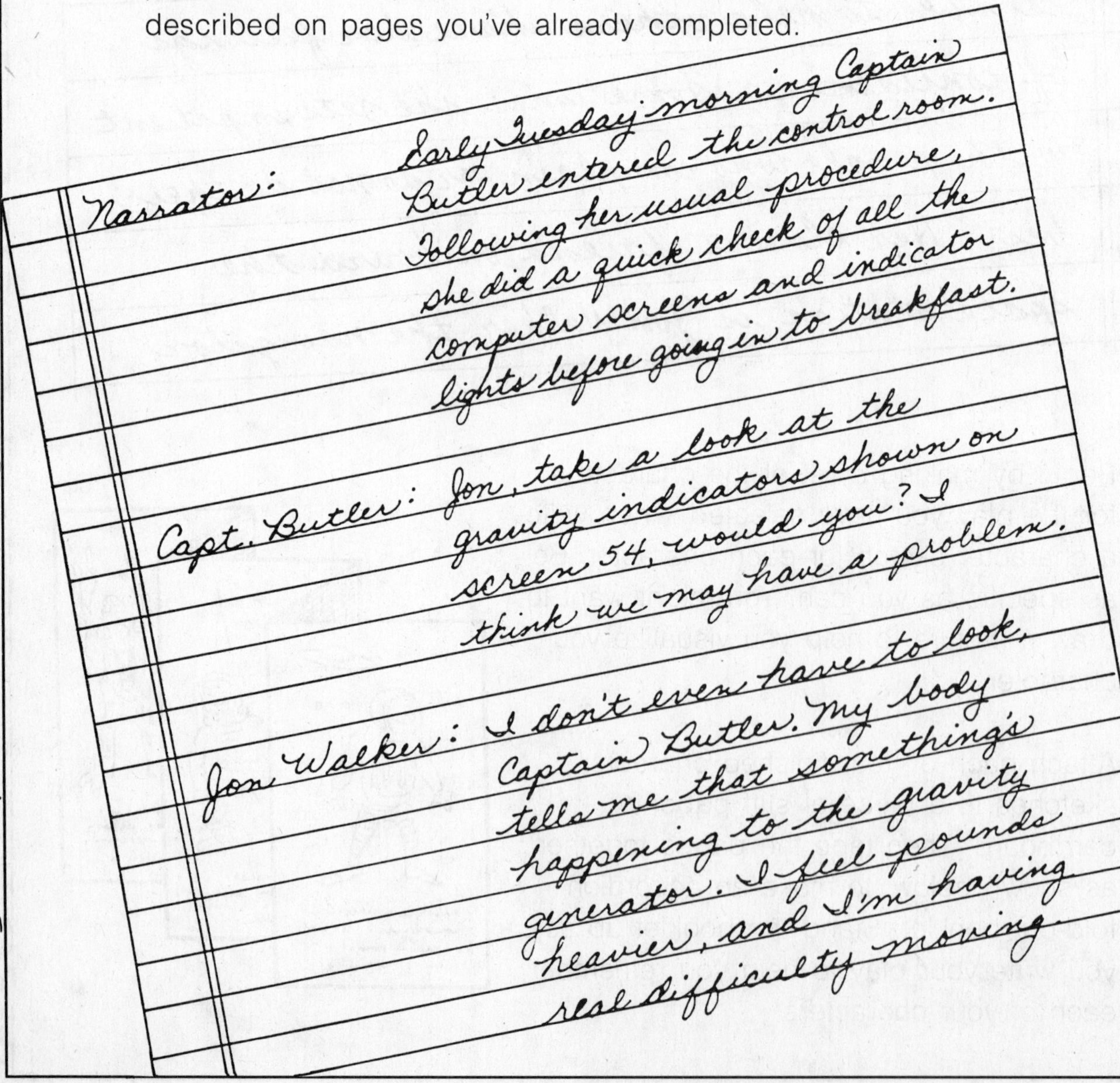

Narrator: Early Tuesday morning Captain Butler entered the control room. Following her usual procedure, she did a quick check of all the computer screens and indicator lights before going in to breakfast.

Capt. Butler: Jon, take a look at the gravity indicators shown on screen 54, would you? I think we may have a problem.

Jon Walker: I don't even have to look, Captain Butler. My body tells me that something's happening to the gravity generator. I feel pounds heavier, and I'm having real difficulty moving.

Macmillan/McGraw-Hill

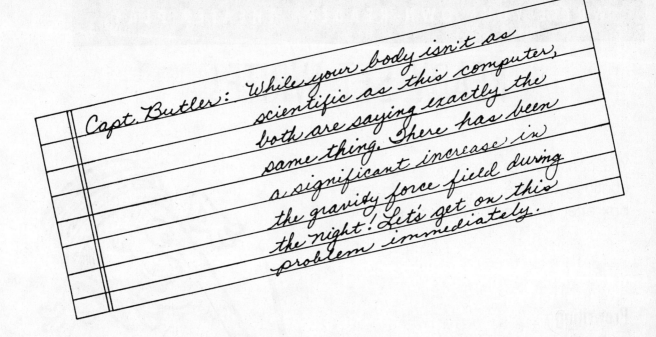

Capt. Butler: While your body isn't as scientific as this computer, both are saying exactly the same thing. There has been a significant increase in the gravity force field during the night! Let's get on this problem immediately.

Use the sample dialog you just read to discuss these questions with a partner or in a small group.

- In what ways does this script differ from a story version of the same event?

- How is the dialog set off?

- What does the narrator's speech do?

- Why is the narrator's speech important?

- Does the dialog for Captain Butler seem to match the character sketch you read on the previous worksheet?

Now try writing a sample of dialog for the play you plan to write. Include speeches from at least two characters and the narrator. Use the character sketches you've created to help you make your characters speak and act appropriately. Remember to use the narrator to identify changes in setting or to describe actions that cannot be written as part of the dialog.

READY, SET, WRITE!

You can use this checklist as you continue to write. Put a check in the box after you complete each step.

Prewriting

☐ Brainstorm ideas for a play.
☐ Outline the plot.
☐ Write the character sketches.

Drafting

☐ Write a first draft of your play. If you work in a group, one person can act as recorder while the others dictate dialog.
☐ Set up your script with the characters' names on the left and the dialog on the right.
☐ Use the narrator to describe action that cannot be written as dialog and to tell about changes in time or place.

Revising

☐ Read your play aloud. Ask these questions: Does the story make sense? Is anything out of order? Should anything be added? Do I have too many or too few characters? Does the dialog sound smooth? Are all the characters believable?
☐ Add interest to your script. Can you add humor or a dialect to make characters come to life?

Macmillan/McGraw-Hill

Proofing

☐ Correct all mistakes in spelling, grammar, punctuation, and script form.

☐ If possible, ask someone else to check your script for errors.

Publishing

☐ Make a final draft of the script. Make sure it is neat and easy to read. Check to make sure all corrections have been made.

☐ Make copies for each member of the cast.

When you reach this point, you're ready to begin rehearsing your Readers Theater play. During rehearsals, listen for suggestions from cast members. Make any changes in the script that you think will improve the play. After the performance, don't forget to take a bow for all your hard work as author!

CHORAL READING
BLOCKING DIAGRAMS

Wish I May
White Horses

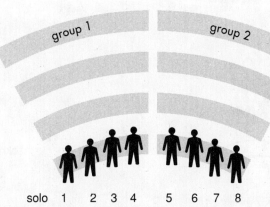

group 1   group 2

solo 1 2 3 4   5 6 7 8

LITTLE TALK

group 1   group 2   group 3

BUT I WONDER...

group 1   group 2

solo 1   2   3   4

The **Q**uestion

group 1   group 2   group 3

group 4

LEVEL 10/UNIT 3

FRIEND

group 1   group 2   group 3

solo   1   2

LEVEL 10/UNIT 4

AND THEY LIVED HAPPILY EVER AFTER <u>FOR A WHILE</u>

group 4   group 5   group 6

group 1   group 2   group 3

solo   1   2

LEVEL 10/UNIT 5
SO WILL I

group 1 group 2 group 3

LEVEL 10/UNIT 5
D⦿⦿R

group 1 group 2

solo

LEVEL 10/UNIT 6
Look, Cinderella!

group 1 group 2

solo 1 2

LEVEL 10/UNIT 6
...And Then the Prince Knelt Down and Tried to Put the Glass Slipper on Cinderella's Foot

group

solo 1 2 3

WISH I MAY

Group 1: Star light, star bright,
First star I've seen tonight,
Wish I may,
Wish I might,
Have this wish I wish tonight.

Group 2: Friday night's dream
On the Saturday told
Is sure to come true,
Be it ever so old.

Group 1: Load of hay, load of hay,
Make a wish and turn away.

Group 2: If wishes were horses,
Then beggars would ride;
If turnips were watches,
I'd wear one by my side.

TRADITIONAL

White Horses

Group 1: *Count the white horses you meet on the way,*
Count the white horses, child, day after day,
Keep a wish ready for wishing—if you
Wish on the ninth horse, your wish will come true.

Solo 1: I saw a white horse at the end of the lane,
Solo 2: I saw a white horse canter down by the shore,
Solo 3: I saw a white horse that was drawing a wain,
Solo 4: And one drinking out of a trough: that made four.

Solo 5: I saw a white horse gallop over the down,
Solo 6: I saw a white horse looking over a gate,
Solo 7: I saw a white horse on the way into town,
Solo 8: And one on the way coming back: that made eight.

Group 2: But oh for the ninth one: where *he* tossed his mane,
And cantered and galloped and whinnied and swished
His silky white tail, I went looking in vain,
And the wish I had ready could never be wished.

Group 1: *Count the white horses you meet on the way,*
Count the white horses, child, day after day,
Keep a wish ready for wishing—if you
Wish on the ninth horse, your wish will come true.

Eleanor Farjeon

LITTLE TALK

Group 1: Don't you think it's probable
that beetles, bugs, and bees
talk about a lot of things—
you know, such things as these:

Group 2: The kind of weather where they live
in jungles tall with grass
and earthquakes in their villages
whenever people pass!

Group 3: Of course, we'll never know if bugs
talk very much at all,
because our ears are far too big
for talk that is so small.

Aileen Fisher

Macmillan/McGraw-Hill

BUT I WONDER...

Solo 1: The crickets in the thickets,
Solo 2: and the katydids in trees,
Solo 3: and ants on plants, and butterflies,
Solo 4: and ladybugs and bees
Group 1: don't smell with little noses
but with *feelers*, if you please.
Group 2: They get along quite nicely,
but I wonder how they *sneeze*.

Aileen Fisher

The Question

1

Group 1: If I could teach you how to fly
Or bake an elderberry pie
Or turn the sidewalk into stars
Or play new songs on an old guitar

Group 2: Or if I knew the way to heaven,
The names of night, the taste of seven
And owned them all, to keep or lend—

Groups 1 & 2: Would you come and be my friend?

2

Group 3: You cannot teach me how to fly.
I love the berries but not the pie.
The sidewalks are for walking on,
And an old guitar has just one song.

Group 4: The names of night cannot be known,
The way to heaven cannot be shown.
You cannot keep, you cannot lend—

Groups 3 & 4: But still I want you for my friend.

Dennis Lee

FRIEND

Group 1: Do you know Paul, Paul Pine (he's nine)
He's really quite . . . unusual.
(The Paul in the house that's next to mine.)
There's something about him that's specially . . . Paul.

Solo 1: Paul has a bike
With a special horn
And you know it's Paul
Who's passing you
(Because of the horn)

Solo 2: And because he calls
(In a special way)
"Come over" (and waves)
Then blows the horn
"Come over right now" (and smiles)
"And play."

Group 2: And you know what Paul
Is trying to say
When he waves and smiles and blows the horn
In that specially Paulish way?

Group 3: It's "I'm your friend
And you're mine too
And there's something quite special
That's specially *you*."

Felice Holman

AND THEY LIVED HAPPILY EVER AFTER FOR A WHILE

Group 1: It was down by the Dirty River
As the Smog was beginning to thin
Because we had been so busy
Breathing the worst of it in,

Group 2: That the worst remained inside us
And whatever we breathed back
Was only—sort of—grayish,
Or at least not entirely black.

Group 3: It was down by the Dirty River
That flows to the Sticky Sea
I gave my heart to my Bonnie,
And she gave hers to me.

Solo 1: I coughed: "I love you, Bonnie.
And do you love me true?"

Groups 1, 2, 3: The tears of joy flowed from my eyes
When she sneezed back:

Solo 2: "Yes—Achoo!"

Group 4: It was high in the Garbage Mountains,
In Saint Snivens by the Scent,
I married my darling Bonnie
And we built our Oxygen Tent.

Macmillan/McGraw-Hill

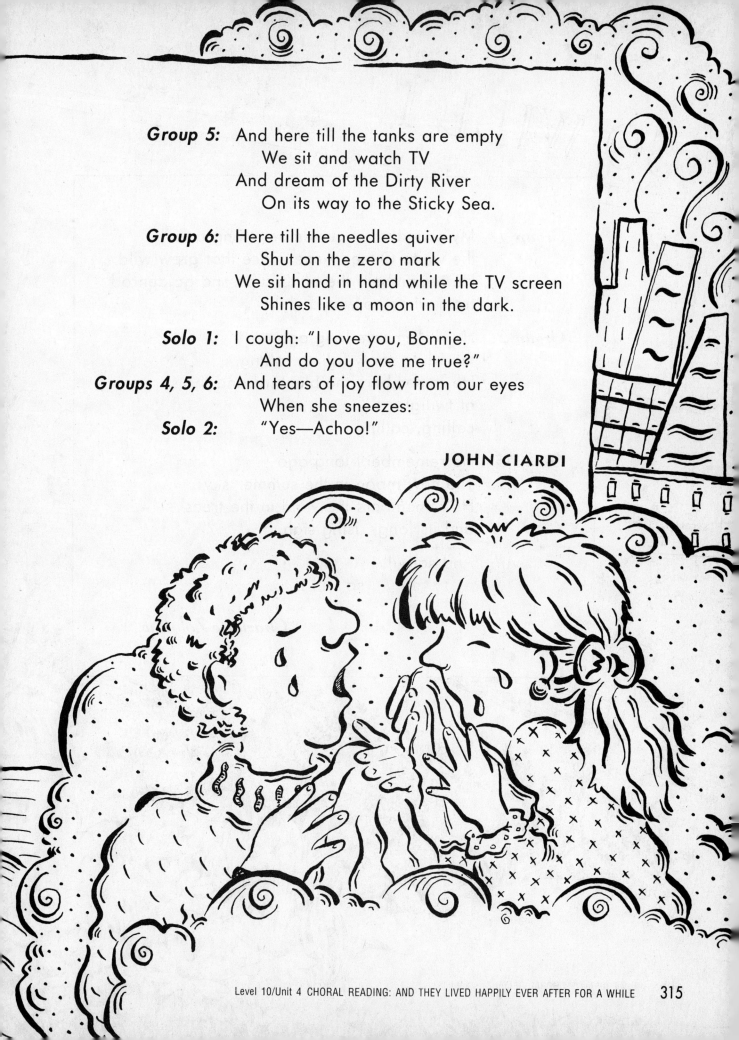

Group 5: And here till the tanks are empty
We sit and watch TV
And dream of the Dirty River
On its way to the Sticky Sea.

Group 6: Here till the needles quiver
Shut on the zero mark
We sit hand in hand while the TV screen
Shines like a moon in the dark.

Solo 1: I cough: "I love you, Bonnie.
And do you love me true?"

Groups 4, 5, 6: And tears of joy flow from our eyes
When she sneezes:

Solo 2: "Yes—Achoo!"

JOHN CIARDI

SO WILL I

Group 1: My grandfather remembers long ago
the white Queen Anne's lace that grew wild.
He remembers the buttercups and goldenrod
from when he was a child.

Group 2: He remembers long ago
the white snow falling falling.
He remembers the bluebird and thrush
at twilight
calling, calling.

Group 3: He remembers long ago
The new moon in the summer sky
He remembers the wind in the trees
and its long, rising sigh.

All: And so will I
so will I.

Charlotte Zolotow

DOOR

Group 1: My grandmother's
Glass front door
Held a fancy pattern
Of panes, their
Heavy edges cut
On a slant:

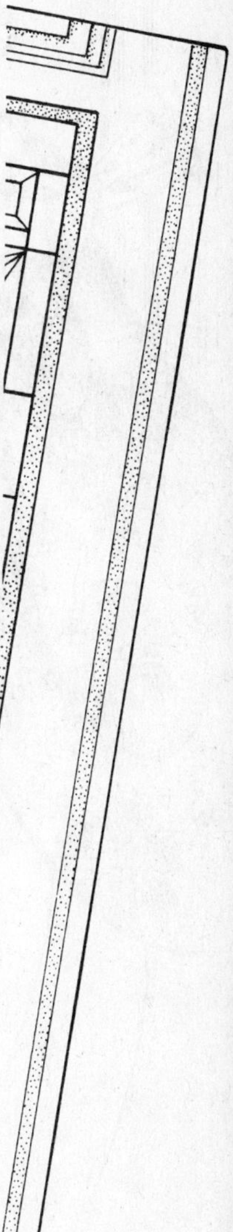

Group 2:   when
Sun shone through,
They scattered
Some eighty little
Flakes of rainbows
Into the room,
Walking the walls,
Glowing like fallen
Flowers on the floor;

Solo: Why don't they
Make front doors that
Way any more?

Valerie Worth

Look, Cinderella!

Solo 1: Look, Cinderella!
　　　　You've lost your glass shoe.
　　I'd go back and fetch it
　　　　With haste, were I you.

Group 1: Pray don't leave it lying;
　　　　It doesn't make sense.
　　The young prince adores you;
　　　　He'll spare no expense
　　To find you, no matter
　　　　How far he must go.

Group 2: Now why cause him anguish
　　　　And worry and woe,
　　And why should you sweep up
　　　　The kitchen with tears
　　And make the prince wander
　　　　For months and for years
　　While both of your stepsisters
　　　　Give themselves airs
　　And you poke the fire and
　　　　Mop the back stairs?

Solo 1: Just pick up your slipper,
　　　　Go back *now* and say,

Solo 2: "My name's Cinderella.
　　　　I wanted to stay.
　　The slipper is mine.
　　　　You can see that it fits."

All: *Hooray, Cinderella! That's using
　　　　your wits.*

Myra Cohn Livingston

Macmillan/McGraw-Hill

...And Then the Prince Knelt Down and Tried to Put the Glass Slipper on Cinderella's Foot

Solo 1: I really didn't notice that he had a funny nose.

Solo 2: And he certainly looked better all dressed up in fancy clothes.

Solo 3: He's not nearly as attractive as he seemed the other night.

All: So I think I'll just pretend that this glass slipper feels too tight.

Judith Viorst

Thinking
ABOUT MY OWN PERFORMANCE

A Reader

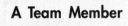
A Listener

A Team Member

Oral-Reading Skills

	ALWAYS	MOST OF THE TIME	SOMETIMES	ALMOST NEVER	NEVER
Did I read my lines fluently?	1	2	3	4	5
Did I mark my script for pauses and special emphasis?	1	2	3	4	5
Did I read with expression?	1	2	3	4	5
Did I read at the correct rate?	1	2	3	4	5
Did I project my voice?	1	2	3	4	5

Listening Skills

	ALWAYS	MOST OF THE TIME	SOMETIMES	ALMOST NEVER	NEVER
Did I listen attentively for my cues?	1	2	3	4	5
Did I listen to myself as I read?	1	2	3	4	5
Did I listen attentively as others read?	1	2	3	4	5
Did I avoid unnecessary movements?	1	2	3	4	5
Did I try to visualize the action and setting?	1	2	3	4	5

Teamwork Skills

	ALWAYS	MOST OF THE TIME	SOMETIMES	ALMOST NEVER	NEVER
Did I come to my team prepared to contribute?	1	2	3	4	5
Did I take turns?	1	2	3	4	5
Did I show respect for others?	1	2	3	4	5
Did I make constructive comments to others?	1	2	3	4	5
Did I consider the suggestions of my teammates?	1	2	3	4	5

Describe one suggestion you used that came from a teammate.

Explain how this suggestion helped you improve your performance.

Select a goal for next time. Write about it.